SAN DIEGO

PetPages

Places to Go & Things to Do with Your Pet

Robert Uherka
Lauren Scott

RJLA, Inc.

<u>Contributing editors</u>
  Jennifer Coburn
  O'Neal Scott

<u>Graphic Illustrators</u>
  Lynda B. Nario
  Nicole Scott

Copyright © 1996 by RJLA, Inc.

ALL RIGHTS RESERVED. No part of this book may be reproduced or transmitted on any form without the written permission of the publisher.

Inquiries and excerpt requests should be addressed to:

  RJLA, Inc.
  9921 Carmel Mountain Rd. #303
  San Diego, CA. 92129
  (619) 484-7930

ISBN # 0-9653148-0-4

Printed and bound in the United States of America.

DISCLAIMER
No liability is assumed by the publisher with respect to the information or contents of this book. Every precaution has been taken to avoid errors, mistakes or omission. Information is destined to change over time and, as such, the publisher does not accept responsibility for errors that may occur.

The publisher has obtained permission to reprint information from the American Animal Hospital Association and the American Veterinary Medical Association.

Attention animal welfare groups, clubs, charitable organizations and all other interested parties. PetPages™ is available at special quantity discounts and makes for an effective fund raising product.
Please call for more information.

Dedications From The Authors

This book is dedicated with much love to my cherished wife, Cynthia, and our unborn son, Trevor. Their sudden death in November of 1995 came just as we had made the commitment to leave our jobs and publish the PetPages in order to spend more time together as a family. I regret that Cynthia could not play an active role in the creation of our mutual dream. But, during what was a very emotionally challenging time, the remembrance of her deep love of animals, her concern for their well being, and her endless passion for life, kept me going forward in producing this book. I was graced by God to have had such a loving wife and supportive friend as I had in her. This book would not exist without her!

To Lauren who stepped in and partnered this project with me. Her childlike energy and laughter have managed to boost my spirits and keep my dream alive.

To my family and friends who have been there when I needed a shoulder to cry on or just a warm hug to renew my faith. For your encouragement and support, I thank you!

And to the rest of my immediate family, my dogs, Bomber and Corky, and cats, Jackson and Freckles. My home would be an empty, and quiet, place without their unconditonal love and the laughter they bring from their unique little personalities.

Robert Uherka

This book is dedicated to Max, whose love and devotion touched my heart in an inexplicable way.

To my wild child Bailey and her girlfriend Taylor, thank you for the joy, laughter, and endless love. Sassy, my precious Kit-Kitty, thank you for putting up with me - I adore you.

A special thank you to those that have supported me and my dreams. Your confidence and encouragement have kept me on my path. My life is so very rich because of you.

Lauren Scott

To Our Readers:

In writing this book, we had one very basic goal - to enrich the lives of pets and their owners. In the process we have spent hours upon hours gathering pertinent pet and local information, putting together helpful maps, creating lists of pet-related services & products, and developing a user friendly format. What we've produced, we feel, is an essential tool to encourage a stronger relationship between dog & cat owners and their pets.

The **PetPages** provides you, the reader, with a variety of useful and exciting information:
- Local places to go with your best friend such as restaurants, parks, beaches, trails, and pet-related events.
- Things to do with your pet such as clubs, games, and events.
- Pet care information & tips covering such topics as travel, first aid, choosing a pet, choosing a vet, photography, grooming, preventative health care, and lost & found pets.
- Complete directory of local services and products, *if it's pet-related you'll find it here!*
- Maps of pet emergency hospitals, restaurants, and parks/trails/beaches.
- Plus...an added feature not found in most books. We've included money saving coupons for all types of products and services.

All this in a handy digest sized book intended to be resourced regularly and taken with you on your pet adventures.

We hope we haven't left out any information or desired material. We urge our readers to write us with any suggestions or new ideas on how to improve our next **PetPages** edition. What you share with us, we can share with thousands of local pet owners striving to enrich the lives of their pets.

Have Fun!

Table of Contents

1 **Calendar of Events**..1

2 **Places to Go**..9
      Social Skills
      Beaches/Lakes
      Hiking
      Camping
      Maps of Area Parks (pages 15-17)
      List of Area Parks (page 18)

3 **Pet-Friendly Restaurants**...37
      Map of Local Restaurants (page 39)
      List of Local Restaurants (page 40)

4 **Exercise & Play**...45
      Tips for Indoor Pets
      Tips for Outdoor Pets
      Exercise & Playtime with Your Dog
      Playtime with Your Car

5 **Clubs & Activities**..63

Breed Shows	Obedience
Junior Showmanship	Agility
Canine Good Citizen	Herding
Field & Hunting	Tracking
Flyball	Frisbee
Lure Coursing	Schutzund
Coonhound	Cat Clubs

6 **Volunteer Opportunities**...73

7 Travel 77
- Packing for Your Pet
- Airplane Travel
- Car Travel
- Hotel Stays
- If Pet is Lost During Travel
- What to Do if You Can't Take Your Pet

8 Pet-Friendly Lodging 91
- Area Lodging Map (page 93)

9 Emergency Care 101
- Accidents
- Pet First Aid
- Natural Disasters
- Emergency Hospital Map (page 109)

10 Lost & Found Pets 111
- Check Inside the House
- Your Search Outside
- Found Pets

11 Weather Tips 115
- Stormy Weather
- Cold Weather
- Hot Weather

12 Photographing Your Pet 119

13 Choosing a New Pet 121
- Are You Ready for a Pet?
- Matching Your Lifestyle With a Pet
- Tips on Adopting a Pet
- Where to Find a Pet
- Questions to Ask About Adoptive Pet

14 New Pet Care..135
Pet Supply Shopping List
Pet-Proofing Your Home
What to Expect . . . the Good, the Bad, & the Ugly
How to Creat Train Your Dog
House-training Your Puppy
Pet Health Signs
Alternatives to Declawing
Kitty Litter Options
Indoor cats

15 Preventative Health Care..153
Finding the Right Veterinarian
Alternative Medicine
Warning Signs
Spay & Neutering
Dental Care
Parasite Control
Nutrition

16 Grooming...179

17 Directory..187

18 Coupons..225
Pet Supplies	Fleas
Restaurants	Lodging
Carpet Cleaning	Day Care
Veterinary Care	Kennels
Pet Sitters	Groomers
Training	

1 Calendar Of Events

There are many pet related events throughout the year in the San Diego area. Information about some of the listed events may be incomplete or may have changed after press time. Please call the phone numbers provided for more details. All telephone numbers are in the (619) area code unless otherwise indicated.

Ongoing

Adopt-A-Pet-On-Sunday. Two Sundays each month, 11:00 a.m. to 3:00 p.m. Located at San Diego County Animal Shelters on a rotating schedule. Call 685-3536 for updates.

September 1996

September 7
Dinner of Champions sponsored by the Escondido Humane Society. This fundraising "Casino Night" evening will be hosted by Tippi Hedron and held at the California Center for the Arts in Escondido at 6:30 p.m. Admission is $40 person or $75 couple. Contact: Stella Hernandez at 745-5747.

September 8
Adopt-A-Pet-In-The-Park sponsored by FOCAS (Friends of County Animal Shelters). To be held at Balboa Park in front of The House of Pacific Relations Building (across from The Organ Pavilion) from 10:30 a.m. to 3:30 p.m. There will be wonderful dogs and beautiful cats looking for a lifetime friend. Contact 685-3536.

September 28 - 29
Puppydog Allstars K-9 Games. Don't miss the qualifying trials at Long Beach University, The Pyramid. There will be games like Musical Chairs, Doggy Dash, Waltzes with Dogs, and Woof Relay. Celebrities, media coverage, demonstrations, and exhibitors will also be there. Contact (707) 745-4237.

September 28
Turf and Tails Auction & Casino Night sponsored by Petco to benefit Canine Companions for Independence. Evening includes entertainment, pasta buffet, gaming, live and silent auction. Tickets purchased before September 20 are $40, after that date they are $45 at the door. Event will be held at the Sports Club at the Del Mar Race Track. For more information, contact Pam Weinstein at 754-3300.

October 1996

Call For Date
First Aid For Pet Owners Seminar sponsored by the San Diego Veterinary Medical Association. The $5 fee proceeds go to animal assistance groups. Call 466-3400 for details.

Call For Date
Semi-Annual Greyhound Roundup & Picnic sponsored by Greyhound Pets of America The event is open to all dogs and their owners. This is the largest get-together of ex-racers in the Western U.S. Meet, mingle, and learn more about Greyhound

Calendar of Events

adoptive programs. Event fee of $10 goes to support the Greyhound rescue program. Event will be held at Miramar NAS. Contact 443-7658.

October 5-6
AKC Agility Trials. To be held at Missile Park in San Diego. Trials run from 8:30 a.m. to 3:00 p.m. For more details, call 561-2434.

October 6
Adopt-A-Pet-In-The-Park sponsored by FOCAS (Friends of County Animal Shelters). To be held at Balboa Park in front of The House of Pacific Relations Building (across from The Organ Pavilion) from 10:30 a.m. to 3:30 p.m. There will be wonderful dogs and beautiful cats looking for a lifetime friend. Contact 685-3536.

October 7
Cocker Spaniel Club of San Diego Specialty Show located at the Kearny Mesa Park & Recreation Center at 3170 Armstrong Street in San Diego. Contact: Chris Wyatt at 484-3368 or Nancy Davis at 266-8754.

October 12
Helen Woodward Animal Center Walk For Animals Fund-Raiser. Join 2,000 pet lovers and their dogs, llamas, lizards, gerbils, and more on this 1 or 2 mile scenic walk through horse country. Registration begins at 7 a.m.; Walk at 8:30 a.m.; Prizes, food, and festivities from 9:30 a.m. to noon. Located at 6525 Calle del Nido, Rancho Santa Fe. Contact Shelly Stuart at 756-4117 for details.

October 13
7th Annual Picnic with Your Pets sponsored by FOCAS (Friends Of County Animal Shelters). Pet contests, great food (vegetarian fare available), super prize drawings: $1,000 - 1st Prize, $500 - 2nd Prize, three $100 3rd Prizes. Lowest cost microchipping will be available — fees include lifetime registration. Held at Morley Field Picnic Pavillion, San Diego (near Balboa Park). $10 each; pets and children under 10 FREE. Contact Norm Friedman at 589-9334.

October 26
Canine Companions for Independence Open House located at the Southwest Regional Center on 124 Rancho del Oro Drive in Oceanside. Contact 754-3300.

November 1996

November 3
Adopt-A-Pet-In-The-Park sponsored by FOCAS (Friends of County Animal Shelters). To be held at Balboa Park in front of The House of Pacific Relations Building (across from The Organ Pavilion) from 10:30 a.m.

to 3:30 p.m. There will be wonderful dogs and beautiful cats looking for a lifetime friend. Contact 685-3536.

November 8
German Shorthaired Pointer Club of San Diego, Inc Specialty Show. Show hours 10 a.m. to 2 p.m. Held at Rancho Santa Fe Polo Grounds. Contact 748-5771.

November 23
Canine Companions for Independence Fall Graduation. Come celebrate the graduation of new recipients and their canine companions for independence. Contact 754-3300.

November 23-24
Southern California Cat Club Cat Show. To be held at the Ramada Inn San Diego North at 5550 Kearny Mesa Road. Admission is $5 for adults and $3 for children and senior citizens. Contact Tim Murphy at 729-9457 for more information.

December 1996

Call For Date
First Aid For Pet Owners Seminar sponsored by the San Diego Veterinary Medical Association. The $5 fee proceeds go to animal assistance groups. Call 466-3400 for details.

December 7
Friends of Cats Open House will feature food, crafts, drawings for gifts, and an opportunity to visit over 300 cats and kittens in the cattery. The Open House will be held from 11:00 a.m. to 3:00 p.m. at 15587 Olde Highway 80 in El Cajon. Contact: 561-0361.

December 8
Adopt-A-Pet-In-The-Park sponsored by FOCAS (Friends of County Animal Shelters). To be held at Balboa Park in front of The House of Pacific Relations Building (across from The Organ Pavilion) from 10:30 a.m. to 3:30 p.m. There will be wonderful dogs and beautiful cats looking for a lifetime friend. Contact 685-3536.

January 1997

January 5
Adopt-A-Pet-In-The-Park sponsored by FOCAS (Friends of County Animal Shelters). To be held at Balboa Park in front of The House of Pacific Relations Building (across from The Organ Pavilion) from 10:30 a.m. to 3:30 p.m. There will be wonderful dogs and beautiful cats looking for a lifetime friend. Contact 685-3536.

January 19
Agility Trial. US Dog Agility Association (USDAA) sponsored trial to be held at Lakeside Junior

Calendar of Events

Arena in Lakeside from 8:30 a.m. to 3:00 p.m. For more details call 561-2434.

February 1997

Call For Date
First Aid For Pet Owners Seminar sponsored by the San Diego Veterinary Medical Association. The $5 fee proceeds go to animal assistance groups. Call 466-3400 for details.

February 2
Adopt-A-Pet-In-The-Park sponsored by FOCAS (Friends of County Animal Shelters). To be held at Balboa Park in front of The House of Pacific Relations Building (across from The Organ Pavilion) from 10:30 a.m. to 3:30 p.m. There will be wonderful dogs and beautiful cats looking for a lifetime friend. Contact 685-3536.

February 22
Annual FOCAS Board Meeting/Breakfast. Friends of County Animal Shelters election of officers. Guest speaker, Paula Hull from the Wild Animal Park, will present a slide program about penguins. The meeting will be held at the La Jolla Tennis & Racket Club in La Jolla. Reservations are required. Contact: Bernice Friedman at 589-9334.

March 1997

March 2
Adopt-A-Pet-In-The-Park sponsored by FOCAS (Friends of County Animal Shelters). To be held at Balboa Park in front of The House of Pacific Relations Building (across from The Organ Pavilion) from 10:30 a.m. to 3:30 p.m. There will be wonderful dogs and beautiful cats looking for a lifetime friend. Contact 685-3536.

March 22-23
AKC Agility Trial. To be held at Missile Park in San Diego from 8:30 a.m. to 3:00 p.m. For more details call 561-2434.

April 1997

Call For Date
First Aid For Pet Owners Seminar sponsored by the San Diego Veterinary Medical Association. The $5 fee proceeds go to animal assistance groups. Call 466-3400 for details.

Call For Date
Helen Woodward Animal Center Open House & Homecoming. Bring the entire family, Fido included, for critter crafts, an agility course for dogs, pooch pool party, tours and more. Enjoy a hot diggity dog lunch for $1. Located at 6525 Calle del Nido, Rancho Santa Fe. Contact 756-4117 for information.

May 1997

Call for Date
Cocker Spaniel Club of San Diego Combined Specialties Show located at the Rancho Santa Fe Polo Grounds at 14555 El Camino Real in Rancho Santa Fe. Contact: Chris Wyatt at 484-3368 or Nancy Davis at 266-8754.

Call for Date
Wagtime Ball sponsored by Rancho Coastal Humane Society. Call 753-6413 for details.

May 22-25
German Shorthaired Pointer Club of America National Specialty Show. Located at 4 Points Hotel on 8110 Aero Drive in San Diego. Show hours are 8 a.m. to 2 p.m. Contact 748-5771.

May 25-26
German Shorthaired Pointer Club of San Diego Inc. Specialty Show. Located at 4 Points Hotel on 8110 Aero Drive in San Diego. Show hours are 10 a.m. to 2 p.m. Contact 748-5771.

June 1997

Call For Date
First Aid For Pet Owners Seminar sponsored by the San Diego Veterinary Medical Association. The $5 fee proceeds go to animal assistance groups. Call 466-3400

Call For Date
The Helen Woodward Animal Center Annual Fling. Guests bid on live and silent auction items, feast on a scrumptious buffet and dance under the stars to live music at this fun event. Located at Fairbanks Village Plaza, outdoors at 6:30 p.m. Tickets: $95 per person.

June 7-8
US Dog Agility Association Trials. To be held at Missile Park in San Diego. Trials run from 8:30 a.m. to 3:00 p.m. For more details, call 561-2434.

August 1997

Call For Date
First Aid For Pet Owners Seminar sponsored by the San Diego Veterinary Medical Association. The $5 fee proceeds go to animal assistance groups. Call 466-3400 for details.

Through August 31
Volunteer Recruitment Month for the Escondido Humane Society. Dog walking, pet grooming, and many more activities will be highlighted this month. Featuring "Each One, Recruit One" and "Bring A Friend." Located at 3000 Las Palmas Avenue in Escondido. Contact: Lee Madrid at 745-5747.

Calendar of Events

September 1997

September 28-29
German Shorthaired Pointer Club of San Diego, Inc. Fall Field Trial. Located at San Jacinto Wildlife Area in Lakeview. Contact 748-5771.

October 1997

Call For Date
First Aid For Pet Owners Seminar sponsored by the San Diego Veterinary Medical Association. The $5 fee proceeds go to animal assistance groups. Call 466-3400 for details.

October 4- 5
NADAC (North American Dog Agility Counsel) Trial. Call 561-2434 for details.

December 1997

Call For Date
First Aid For Pet Owners Seminar sponsored by the San Diego Veterinary Medical Association. The $5 fee proceeds go to animal assistance groups. Call 466-3400 for details.

Pet Pages

2 Places to Go

Pets are welcome in many outdoor public areas. Including your pet in your outings can be exciting for both of you. Just watching his pleasure is enjoyment in itself. Plan ahead and have fun!

- Be sure pet is in good health and has current vaccinations.
- Pick up after pet.
- Have well mannered pet (not aggressive).
- Keep pet on leash.
- Don't allow pet to bother others.
- Bring water & bowls.
- Check pet for fleas, ticks, burrs, and other hazards.
- Never take your pet out of your home without some form of identification. You don't go anywhere without your ID, neither should your pet.

Social Skills

Wherever you take your pet, you will most likely encounter other dogs and their owners. In general, most dogs behave when they meet on neutral ground. However, always exercise caution when you or your pet meet a new dog. Here are a few tips to help avoid possible dog fights.

Tips on Avoiding Dog Fights

- Prevent fights by keeping your dog on a leash.
- As you approach other leashed dogs, be sure there is ample room between them.
- Don't approach dogs without their owner's permission.
- Even with permission, approach a new dog with caution.

How to Break Up a Dog Fight

- Respond quickly, but do not endanger your safety.
- Make a loud noise to distract dogs, or douse them both with water.
- Do not get in the middle of the fight or even close to the fighting dogs — keep a safe distance or you may be accidentally bitten.
- If your dog is wounded in a fight, rinse cuts and abrasions with a solution of water and peroxide. Call your veterinarian.

Beaches/Lakes

Some dogs absolutely love to swim and there are others that are less than thrilled at the thought of getting wet. DO NOT ASSUME ALL DOGS KNOW HOW TO SWIM. Be prepared to assist if your pet seems unsure. With some support and encouragement from you, a willing pet will quickly catch on. For those pets that will fetch, throwing a tennis ball or any other floatable toy out in the water is great fun and exercise. Watch for any signs of fatigue. Dogs can drown from exhaustion. Be sure that your pet has a safe path into the water. Slippery rocks, broken glass, fallen branches, or other sharp objects in or around water's edge can be extremely hazardous. Also, be aware that many of these objects could be out of eyesight, just below the water's surface. Bring fresh water for pet to drink. Parasites and bacteria found in lakes, streams, and salt water can be harmful to your pet.

Water Tips

- Be careful of strong currents or rip tides.
- Never throw or frighten dog into water.

- Use specially formulated pet sunscreen on dogs with light-colored hair in the areas of their nose and ears, where the hair is thin and the skin is more exposed (pets are subject to sunburns and skin cancer).

- Rocky or steep embankments can be dangerous or hard for tired pets.

- Some dogs may be frightened by large waves found on the ocean beaches but are fine at calmer waters such as lakes and streams. Be sensitive to their fears.

Hiking

Hiking with your pet is wonderful exercise and fun for you and your pet. Not only will your pet enjoy the adventure of new sights and smells, but you'll enjoy watching his enthusiasm. Who knows what new things you'll discover by watching him uncover smelly treasures in the brush.

As with any exercise, begin slowly allowing your pet to gradually increase his stamina. Monitor the distance of the hike. You know your pet's health and how far he can go. Don't push past that point or you may end up carrying him back. If he shows signs of tiring — stop! Be sure that you bring plenty of water for him to drink throughout the hike. On warm days, be sure to rest in shady spots. Don't let pets overheat; they depend on you to slow them down. Pets don't realize that if they keep running, they'll drop from exhaustion. If your pet does overheat, you need to cool him down immediately. Find shade and give him water. If possible, submerge him in water. See EMERGENCY SECTION for what to do for heat stroke.

Remember pets can suffer from sore muscles and joints from overdoing it, just like us. If you notice your pet moving slowly the next day, check with your vet-

Places to Go

erinarian to be sure. If he has sore muscles, encourage your pet to do a little stretching, take a short walk, and pamper him with a gentle massage; he will love you for it!

Keep your pet safe under watchful care. Always keep pet in sight even in areas where pets are allowed off leash. There are many possible dangers like poisonous snakes, insects, traffic, and animals that could harm your pet.

You have hiking boots, now your pet can too. For pet's comfort, you may want to purchase dog boots. It sounds funny but they really make a difference. Your pet will get used to them and appreciate them. If your pet prefers to rough it, be sure to check his feet regularly for cracks, blisters, or any debris that may be caught between toes. Frequent checks are especially important if you are hiking on rough terrain with sharp rocks, sticks, or pine cones. Even the most experienced dog can develop tender paws.

Backpacks are available for dogs. Before purchasing one for your pet, think about the following. Is your dog large enough to carry one and is he in shape to take on the additional weight? Backpacks may be too much for many small dogs. If you have any questions, please consult your veterinarian. If you decide to use a dog backpack, be careful not to overload it to the point of stressing your dog's back and muscles. Dogs carrying the extra weight can overexert themselves and end up with sore muscles or possible injuries.

Watch out for poison oak. Although it may not bother your pet, he can bring it back to you and back to your home and family. By gathering the itchy oils on his fur, you may unknowingly pet the oils onto your skin. A bath after hiking in areas that may contain poison oak is recommended.

At the conclusion of your hike, check your pet for ticks, fleas, foxtail, scratches, or any other problems.

Hiking Tips

- For pet's safety, don't allow pets to interact with wildlife.
- Depending on the length of the hike, bring snacks or food for your pet.
- Bring water for your pet. Discourage pet from drinking water from lakes or streams. These other water sources may contain harmful bacteria.
- Check pet's feet frequently for any soreness.
- Monitor pet's pace; allow time for rest and water as needed.

Camping Tips

For the safety of your pet, he should sleep in the tent with you. Most camp sites will require it. Tying pets up outside leaves them vulnerable to wild animals. He may also escape and get lost. After all, why do you think they call them pup tents?

For the comfort of your pet, consider bringing a mat or two for him to lay on inside and outside of the tent. Many campsites are either rocky or bare dirt. Very seldom do you find a grassy shady spot for Rover to rollover!

Welcome to the PetPages™ Guide to PARKS, BEACHES, & TRAILS in the San Diego area.

Following you'll find map locations and descriptions of parks, beaches, and trails that we are aware of in the San Diego area. If we have not listed your favorite play area, please contact us so we may included it in our next edition.

Don't forget to always bring the **PetPages**™ with as your resource for additional information on places to eat, emergency care and first aid, and other pet-related services.

Enjoy!!!

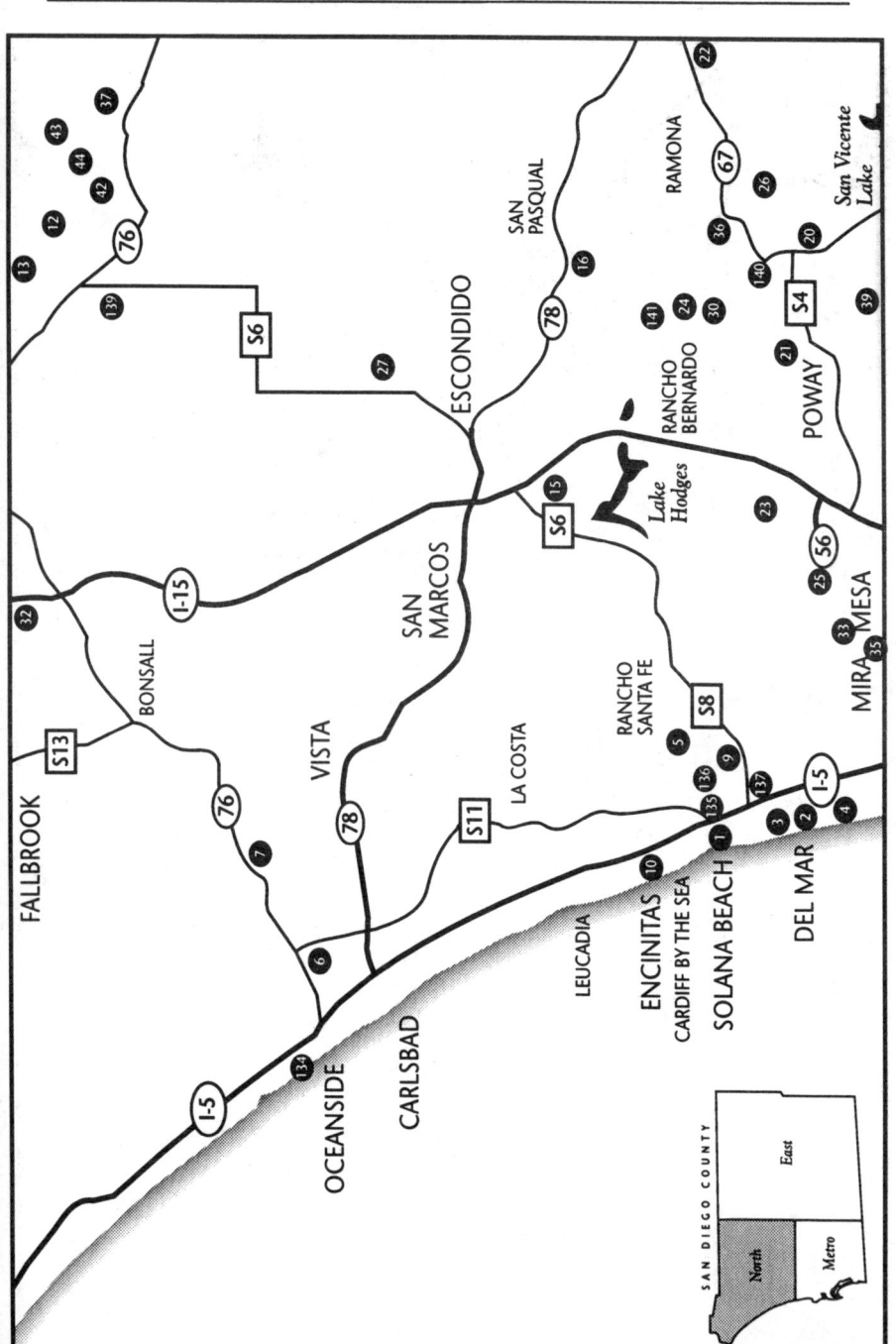

Places to Go 17

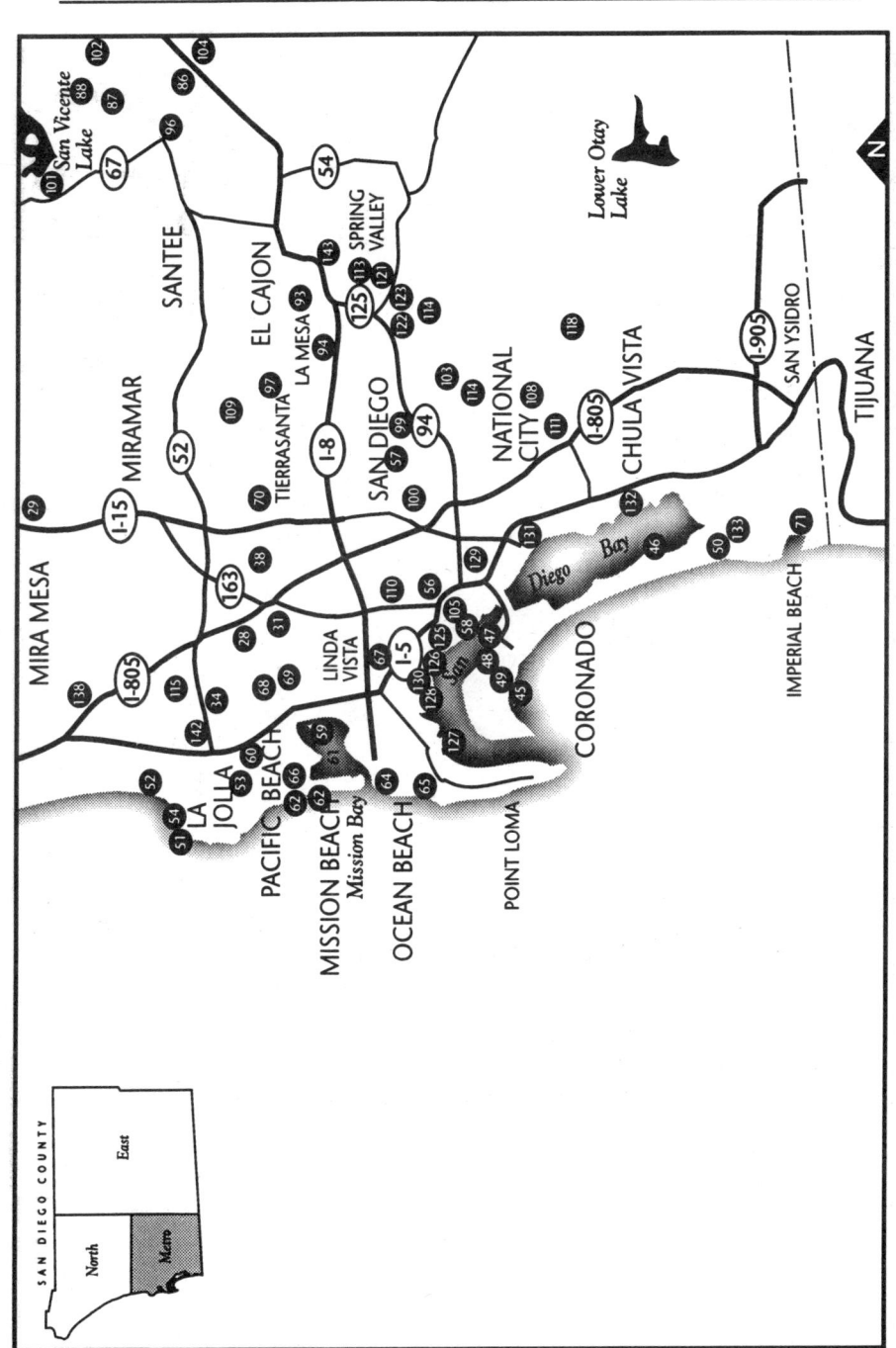

18　　　　　　　　　Pet Pages

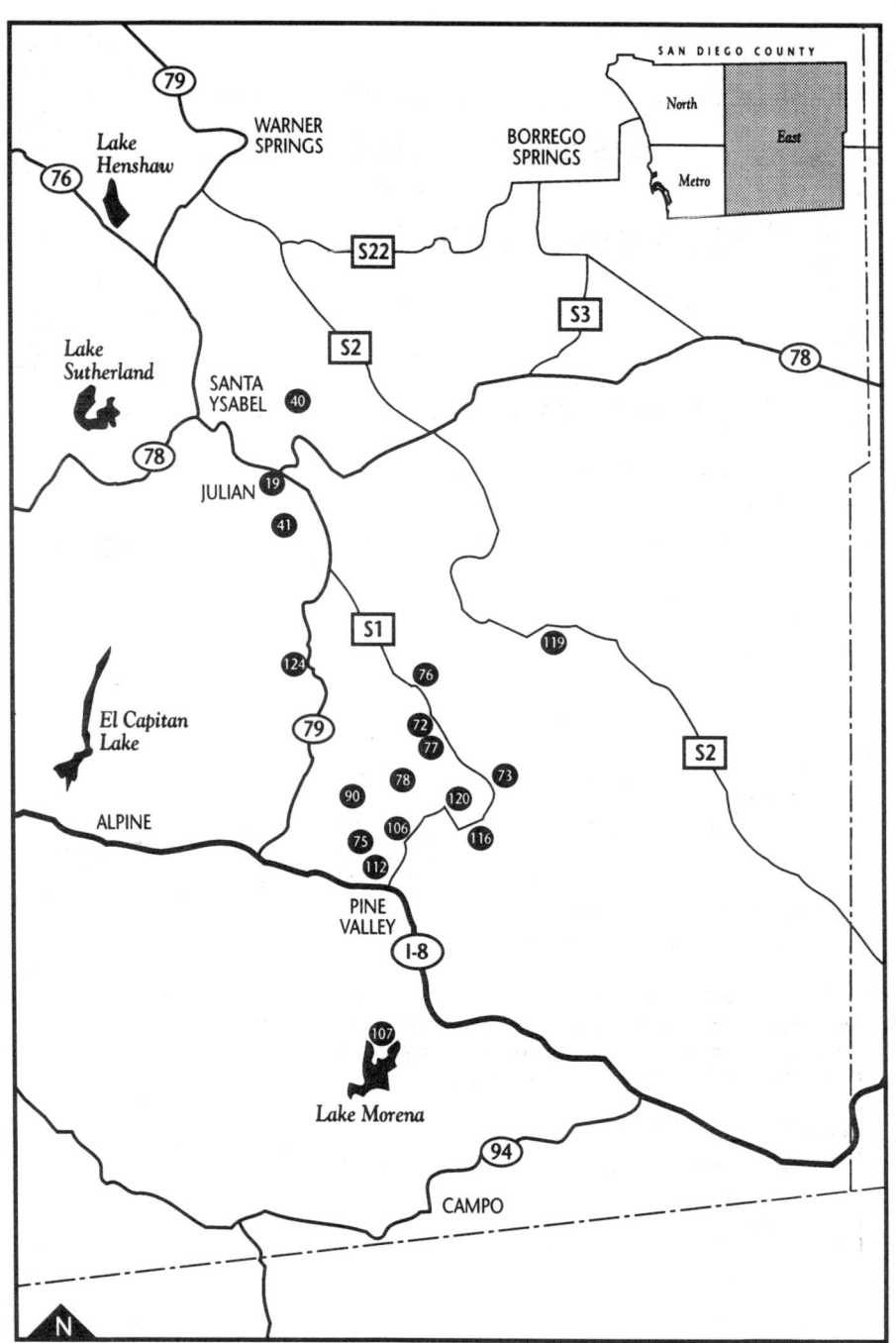

Places to Go

PARKS, BEACHES & TRAILS
Legend

- No Leash Required!!!
- Swimming allowed
- Hiking trails
- Camping sites
- Fishing permitted or sites close by.

S = Small   M = Medium   L = Large
Designates the size of area and length of trails available for play & exercise.

Cardiff by the Sea
1 Cardiff State Beach
Leash required. One of the few beaches in North County that allows dogs. Old Hwy 101 west of San Elijo Lagoon. **753-5091** *M*

Del Mar
2 Del Mar Beach - Mid section
No dogs allowed from June 1st to Sept 30th. Leashed dogs are allowed from Oct 1st to May 31st. Located in Del Mar along the beach from 17th St. to 29th St. **755-1556** *M*

Del Mar
3 Del Mar Beach - North End
Three Barks For This Beach! Well, at least part of the year dogs can run free without leashes. Located just west of the race track by the bluffs. Leashes are required from June 1st to Sept 30th. From Oct 1st to June 1st, leashes are not required. The North End begins at 29th Street and runs north to Solana Beach. **755-1556** *M*

Del Mar
4 Del Mar Beach - South End
Leashes required. Regardless of the leash rule, this beach is worth visiting anyway. Make sure you have a pooper scooper with you as they are concerned about anything left behind. Located along the beach from 6th St. to 17th St. **755-1556** *M*

Encinitas
5 Pacific Scene Recreation Trail (Also called Brookside Trail)
This 4 mile trail follows along the Escondido Creek giving you a scenic hike with Rover. Take I-5 to Encinitas Blvd. Go east to Rancho Santa Fe Rd. left to Lone Jack then left to Camino del Rancho. Park is at the intersection. **633-2740** *M*

Pet Pages

Oceanside
6 Buddy Todd Memorial Park
Leashes required. Pretty, little grassy park. Take Hwy 76 east 1.5 miles to Butler St. go right to Barnwell turn left and go to Mesa, turn left and then another left into the park. Thomas Bros. 1086, E6. **966-4520** *S*

Oceanside
7 Guajome Regional Park
Leash required. 569 acres with a marsh and spring fed lakes. Dogs are not allowed on trails. Interstate 5 to Hwy 76 go east 7 miles to Guajome Lakes Rd. south to park entrance. Thomas Bros. 1087, F2. **694-3049** *L*

San Diego
8 Memorial Community Park
Leash required. Located at Marcy Ave. and Oceanview Blvd. Take Hwy 5 south to National Ave. east to 30th St. north to park. Thomas Bros. 1289, E5. **235-1125** *S*

San Diego
9 San Dieguito Regional Park
Leash required. This 125 acre park offers picnic areas and hiking through chaparral. Take Interstate 5 north to Lomas Santa Fe Dr. east one mile to Sun Valley Rd. then north to the park entrance. Thomas Bros. 1168, A6. **694-3049** *M*

San Diego
10 San Elijo State Beach
Leashed required. Dog-friendly area starts south of life guard tower 7. **Take I-5 to Manchester exit, go west to Hwy. 101 south to beach .** *M*

Cleveland National Forest
11 Crosley Trail - Palomar District
2.6 miles. Begins at Crosley Saddle and descends NE to a dead end at private property. **673-6180** *M*

Cleveland National Forest
12 Cutca Trail - Palomar District
2.5 miles. Western end of trail begins where the Palomar-McGee trail stops. Just east of Eagle Crag. Shade and a stream are found on this canyon trail. Hwy 79 at Aguanga. **673-6180** *M*

Cleveland National Forest
13 Dripping Springs Trail - Palomar District
About 7 miles of trail. Interstate 15 (N) to Hwy 79 in Temecula go east to Aqua Tibia Wilderness area. Start at Dripping Springs Campground. The elevation climbs from 1,600 feet to 4,400 feet. **673-6180** *L*

Places to Go   21

Cleveland National Forest
14 Palomar- McGee Trail - Palomar District
5.5 miles. Going south on the crest of the Agua Tibia Mt., the trail reaches an elevation of 5,000 feet allowing several views of the Pacific Ocean and coastal hills. Call for maps. **673-6180** *L*

Escondido
15 Felicita Regional Park
Leash required. This park features large oaks, freshwater streams and boulder-strewn hillsides. Interstate 15 to Via Rancho Parkway go west one mile to Felicita Rd. then north one mile to park entrance. Thomas Bros. 1149, H1. **694-3049** *M*

Escondido
16 San Dieguito River Park
Leashes required. There are over 30 miles of beautiful trails ranging from easy to difficult with beautiful views of the area. Interstate 15 to Hwy 78 east. 5.5 miles past the San Diego Wild Animal Park. The parking area is on the south side of the hwy. *L*

Fallbrook
17 Alturas
Leash required. Walking paths are available. Located off Mission Rd. in Fallbrook. Turn left on W. Fallbrook St. to Alturas south to park. Thomas Brothers 1027, E3. **694-3049** *S*

Fallbrook
18 Fallbrook Community Park
Leash required. Take Mission Rd. north to W. Fallbrook St. east to park. Thomas Bros. 1027, H3. **694-3049** *S*

Julian
19 Inaja National Recreation Trail Hike
Stretch your legs on this short ½ mile trail. Leash required. From Julian head west on Hwy 79/78 to the Inaja picnic area. *S*

Poway
20 Iron Mountain Trail Hike
Over 6 miles of trails requiring 3-4 hours will challenge beginners. There are ocean views from the 2,956 foot summit. Poway Rd. east to Hwy. 67. Turn right, parking on eastern shoulder of hwy. *M*

Poway
21 Poway Community Dog Park
No leash required! Three fenced grass areas are designated for dog play. Very nice setting to watch Fido play with others of his kind. Take I-15 to Poway Rd. go east about 5 miles to Bowron Rd. go right to 13094 Bowron Rd. Thomas Bros. 1190, D5. *S*

Pet Pages

Ramona
22 Collier
Leash required. Oldest park in county system. Take Hwy 78 to Ramona turn right on 7th St. 2 blocks. Thomas Brothers 1152, H6. **694-3049** *S*

San Diego
23 Black Mountain Open Space
200 acres. Leashes required. Hang gliders can be seen soaring around some days. Interstate 15 to Rancho Penasquitos Blvd. go west 2 miles to Black Mountain Rd. go right 2 miles (N) to dead end. Turn right on the dirt road and follow to paved parking area. **525-8281** *L*

San Diego
24 Blue Sky Ecological Preserve Hike
3 mile path along a shaded creekside. Leash required. Interstate 15 north exit Poway Rd. go east to Espola Rd. turn left (N) pass Lake Poway .5 miles to entrance. Thomas Bros. 1171, A2. *M*

San Diego
25 Canyonside Community Park
6' Leash required. Take Hwy 15 to Mercy Rd. west to Black Mountain Rd. north to park. Thomas Bros. 1189, D6. **538-8131** *S*

San Diego
26 Dos Picos Regional Park
Leash required. 79 acres of extensive oak woodland. Northeast of San Diego. Hwy 67 north to Mussey Grade Rd. south one mile to Dos Picos Park Rd. follow for one mile to entrance. Thomas Bros. 1171, H5. **694-3049** *L*

San Diego
27 Hellhole
Leash required. Over 1,700 acres of rugged preserve. Several miles of hiking trails traverse the mixed chaparral. I-15 north to Valley Pkwy. East 6 miles to Lake Wohlford Rd. 3 miles east to Paradise Mt. Rd. East .5 miles to Kiavo Rd. then .5 miles to entrance. **694-3049** *L*

San Diego
28 Kearney Mesa Community Park
Leash required. Located at Armstrong St. and Mesa College Dr. Take Hwy 805 north to Balboa Ave. go west to Genesee to park. Adjacent to Tecolote Canyon Park. Thomas Bros. 1248, J5. **573-1387** *S*

San Diego
29 Lake Miramar
Leashes required. Walk, bike, rollerblade, or jog around the 5 mile lake. Can get crowded on weekends. Open 7 days a week from sunrise to sunset. East of Interstate 15 in Scripps Ranch. On Scripps Lake Dr. off of Scripps Ranch Blvd. **668-2050** *M*

Places to Go   23

San Diego
30 Lake Poway Recreation Area
Leash required. This is the hub for a 60 mile trail system in and around the city of Poway. Off Lake Poway Rd. off Espola in Poway. Thomas Bros. 1170, H4. **679-5466** *M*

San Diego
31 Linda Vista Community Park
Leash required. Located at Levant St. off Linda Vista Rd. Take Hwy 163 north to Genesee Ave. west to park. Thomas Bros. 1248, J6. **573-1392** *S*

San Diego
32 Live Oak Regional Park
Leash required. Featuring 25 acres of oak trees and 2 miles of hiking trails, this is a favorite picnic destination. Interstate 15 to Hwy 76 go west 2.7 miles to Gird Rd. then 3.5 miles north to park entrance. Thomas Bros. 1028, C4. **694-3049** *M*

San Diego
33 Los Penasquitos Canyon Preserve Hike
Over 7 miles of fairly flat trails for hikers to explore. Leash required. Creekside trails, pools, waterfalls. Interstate 15 to Mercy Rd. west to Black Mountain Rd. Plenty of parking. West side take Sorento Valley Rd. 1 mile east of interstate 805. **484-7504** *L*

San Diego
34 Marian Bear Memorial Park
Leash required. Running the length of San Clemente Canyon, it features over 466 acres of open space. Off Hwy 52 either from Regents Rd. or Genesee Ave. Thomas Bros. 1248, B1. **581-9952** *L*

San Diego
35 Mira Mesa Community Park
Leash required. Located at New Salem St. and Mira Mesa Blvd. **538-8122** *S*

San Diego
36 Mount Woodson
Views of Poway and the Pacific. Great rock climbing. Over 3½ miles of trails. Interstate 15 north to Poway Rd exit go east to Hwy 67. turn left (N) go 3 miles to a California Division of Forestry fire station. Park across the station on dirt turnouts. *M*

San Diego
37 Palomar County Park
Leash required. Small 2 acre park, surrounded by scenic mountain forest. Take County Rd S-6 north from Hwy. 76 to S-7. East to Crestline then north to the park. **694-3049** *S*

San Diego
38 Serra Mesa Community Park
Leash required. Located at Village Glen and Glencolumn Drs. Take Hwy 163 north to Aero Dr.

east to park. Thomas Bros. 1249, D4. **573-1408** *S*

San Diego
39 Sycamore
Leash required. Several miles of trails cover this rugged terrain. Oak groves add diversity to the chaparral and coastal sage. I-15 to Poway Rd. go east to Garden Rd. then right on Sycamore Canyon Rd. turns into a dirt road continue to end. **694-3049** *L*

San Diego
40 Volcan
Leash required. A rustic viewpoint and natural stone gateway grace the entrance of this 228 acre preserve. From Julian take Farmer Rd. 3 miles north past Wynola Rd. to the Access Rd. to entrance. Thomas Bros. 1136, D2. **694-3049** *L*

San Diego
41 William Heise Regional Park
Leash required. Over 900 acres of pine, oak and cedar in a mountainous surrounding. Miles and miles of hiking. Northeast of San Diego. From Hwy 78/79 one mile west of Julian, take Pine Hills Rd south for 2 miles to Frisius Rd. Go east another 2 miles. **694-3049** *L*

San Marcos
42 Love Valley
It takes about an hour to complete the 2 mile trail found in this park. Quiet spots can be found to relax with your best friend. North on Interstate 15 then east on Hwy 76 to East Grade Rd go left about 3 miles to a turnout on the south side of the road. Starts at the locked gate. *M*

San Diego
43 Obseratory Trail
Warm up your sneakers on this 2 mile trail. North on Interstate 15 then east on Hwy 76. Go east on South Grade Rd. (S6) to the Palomar Observatory. *M*

San Diego
44 Thunder Springs Trail
Stretch your legs on this 4 mile trail. Loop past a beautiful pond and some great views. North on Interstate 15 to 76 east. north on South Grade Rd. (S6) then west on East Grade Rd (S7) to park entrance and office. Doane Pond parking area. *M*

Coronado
45 Coronado Beach - North End
Yeah! Dogs are permitted off leash south of naval base and north of life guard tower. A favorite spot you'll want to check out. Find Hotel Del Coronado and go west to a dead end. Enjoy! **522-7380** *M*

Coronado
46 Coronado Cays Park
Requires 6' leash, park closes 11 pm each day. Coronado Cays Blvd. and Grand Caribe Cswy. Thomas Bros. 1329, D1. **522-7342** *S*

Places to Go   25

Coronado
47 Coronado Tidelands Regional Park
Leash required. Bayside grassy park with a beach area. Cross the bridge, first right onto Glorietta Blvd. Turn right into park on Mullinix Dr. **686-6222** *M*

Coronado
48 Glorietta Bay Park
Requires 6', park closes 11 pm each day. Just off the Silver Strand by the bay. Strand Way north of Naval Base. Thomas Bros. 1308, J1. **522-7342** *S*

Coronado
49 Spreckles Park
Requires 6' leash. Park closes 11 p.m. each day. Located at 6th St. and Orange Ave. Thomas Bros. 1288, H6. **522-7342** *S*

Imperial Beach
50 Imperial Beach - South
Leash required. Dogs are allowed south of Imperial Beach Blvd. and north of Palm Ave. Thomas Bros. 1329, E7. *M*

La Jolla
51 Ellen Browning Scripps Park
Leash required. Dogs allowed before 9 a.m. or after 6 p.m. Located at Coast Blvd. and Girard. Downtown La Jolla off from Prospect St. Thomas Bros. 1227, F6. **221-1129** *S*

La Jolla
52 La Jolla Shores Beach
Leash required. Great place to watch surfers, take in the sea breeze, or just stroll down the beach. Dogs are allowed before 9 a.m. and after 6 p.m. Located west of Camino del Oro in La Jolla Shores. Thomas Bros. 1227, H4. *M*

La Jolla
53 Mount Soledad Park
Leashes required. Not much exercise here but, the views are to die for! This park offers incredible views of the area. From the north take I-5 to Ardath west to Hidden Valley (left) to top. South take Nautilus St. east to South St. take Soledad Rd. **552-1568** *S*

La Jolla
54 Point La Jolla Cliffs and Beaches
Leashes required. A nice area to either watch the sunset from the cliffs or take stairs down to the beach area. Dogs permitted before 9 a.m. and after 6 p.m. Located at Coast Blvd. and Girard Ave. **221-8901** *S*

Pet Pages

National City
55 Lincoln Acres
Leash required. Take 805 south to Plaza Blvd. go east to Euclid, turn south to Ridgeway turn left to Granger then turn right to park. Thomas Bros. p.1310, C3. **694-3049** *S*

San Diego
56 Balboa Park
Two areas <u>don't require leashes</u>. West side of park near the lawn bowling and at Morley Field. All other areas require a leash. This large park is great for miles of walking pleasure. Hwy 163 and I-5. Several exits will get you there. TB 1289, D1. **239-1100** *L*

San Diego
57 Colina del Sol Community Park
6' Leash required. Located at Orange Ave. and 54th St. Take Hwy 94 east to 54th St. north to park. Thomas Bros. 1270, B4. **235-1144** *S*

San Diego
58 Embarcadero Marina Park
Leashes required. Enjoy the surroundings! Small park near Seaport Village. Southwest end of downtown. Off Kettner Blvd. on the bay. Thomas Bros. 1288, J4. **291-3900 ext222** *S*

San Diego
59 Fiesta Island
Dogs are allowed off leash on the whole island! Lots of sand and water for a guaranteed good time. Take I-5 to Sea World Dr. exit. take Fiesta Island Rd. onto the island. Road goes all the way around the island. **221-8901** *L*

San Diego
60 Kate O. Sessions Park
Leashes required. This grassy hillside park offers beautiful views of the city. Located at Soledad Rd. and Park Dr. near Pacific Beach. Park hours: 9 a.m. - 10 p.m. Thomas Bros. 1248, A4. **581-9924** *S*

San Diego
61 Mission Bay Park
Leashes required. Beautiful grassy areas along with sandy beaches to walk around. Dogs permitted before 9 a.m. or after 6 p.m. Entry points all around the park. One entry is by taking Interstate 5 to Clairemont Dr. exit go west. Thomas Bros. 1268, C3. **221-8901** *L*

San Diego
62 Mission Beach/ Pacific Beach
Leashes required. Dogs allowed before 9 a.m. or after 6 p.m. Miles of beach to stroll. Interstate 5 exit Garnett west to Pacific Beach. Mission Beach is south of this all the way to Mission Bay Channel. **221-8901** *L*

Places to Go 27

San Diego
63 Montgomery - Waller Park
Leash required. Located at Coronado Ave. and Beyer Blvd. Take Hwy 5 south to Coronado Ave. go east to park. Thomas Bros. 1350, D1. **424-0466** *S*

San Diego
64 Ocean Beach Park/ Dog Park
Dog Beach! Off leash year-round. All other areas of Ocean Beach allow dogs leashed before 9 A.M. and after 6 P.M. Interstate 5 to Interstate 8 west. Follow signs to Sunset Cliffs Blvd. turn right on Voltaire St.. Thomas Bros. 1267, H5. **221-8901** *M*

San Diego
65 Ocean Beach Recreation Center
Leash required. Located at Santa Monica Ave. and Ebers St. just off Sunset Cliffs Blvd. Thomas Bros. 1267, J6. **531-1527** *S*

San Diego
66 Pacific Beach Recreation Center
Leash required. Located at Diamond and Gresham St. Take Hwy 5 to Grand Exit go west to Haines St. go north to park. Thomas Bros. 1247, J5. **581-9927** *S*

San Diego
67 Presidio Park
Leashes required. Shady trails on historic park. Close to downtown. Interstate 8 to Taylor St. exit west turn left on Presidio Dr. takes you into park. **297-3258** *M*

San Diego
68 South Clairemont Park
Leash required. Located at Clairemont Dr. south of Balboa Ave. Take Hwy 5 north to Balboa Ave. go east to Clairemont Dr. south to park. Thomas Bros. 1248, E4. **581-9924** *S*

San Diego
69 Tecolote Canyon Natural Park
Leashes required. 9 acres of natural history. Hike can be tough in some areas but, worth the effort. Interstate 5 exit at Seaworld Dr. go east to park. Thomas Bros. 1248, F4. **581-9952** *M*

San Diego
70 Tierrasanta Park
Leash required. Located at Clairemont Mesa Blvd. near La Cuenta Dr. Take Hwy 15 north to Clairemont Mesa Blvd. east to park. Thomas Bros. 1249, J1. **573-1393** *S*

San Diego
71 Tijuana River National Estuarine
Leash required. This 2,500 acre salt marsh is home to over 350 species of migratory birds. Dogs allowed on specified trails only. Interstate 5 to Coronado Ave. exit go south at the light. Go 1.5

28 Pet Pages

miles on Hollister to Sunset Ave. turn west then south on Saturn. Thomas Bros. 1349,H5.
575-3613 *L*

Cleveland National Forest
72 Big Laguna Trail · Descanso District
Leash required. Starts near the Laguna Campground parking lot. 1 mile into the park you'll find Big Laguna Lake and a beautiful meadow. (The lake usually has water in it.) Connects to other trails. Call for park maps & directions. **445-6235** *L*

Cleveland National Forest
73 Desert View Nature Trail · Descanso District
Leash required. Trail begins in Burnt Rancheria Campground and follows along the rim of chaparral covered mountain. Excellent views of the desert floor 4,000 feet below. Salton Sea can be seen on a clear day. Call for a map/directions. **445-6235** *L*

Cleveland National Forest
74 Espinosa Trail · Descanso District
Leash required. 6.4 miles. The majority of the trail traverses chaparral but one section is in an oak-riparian woodland. Remote camping. Call for park maps & directions. **445-6235** *L*

Cleveland National Forest
75 Horsethief Trail · Descanso District
Leash required. This 1.2 mile trail is located near the north end of the Horsethief Rd. and is an access point into the Pine Creek Wilderness Area. Be aware that some of the trail is considered strenuous. Call for a map/directions. **445-6235** *L*

Cleveland National Forest
76 Kwaaymii Cultural Trail · Descanso District
Leash required. Short, yet beautiful hike. Overlooks Cottonwood Canyon. Take I-8 east to Sunrise Hwy. go north to the Pioneer Mail Picnic area. **445-6235** *M*

Cleveland National Forest
77 Lightning Ridge Trail · Descanso District
Leash required. 1.3 miles starting at the Laguna Campground and winds through pine and oak trees to a hilltop overlooking the Laguna Meadow areas. It's a fairly strenuous climb. Call for park maps & directions. **445-6235** *M*

Cleveland National Forest
78 Noble Canyon Trail · Descanso District
Leash required. 10 mile trail begins along Pine Creek Rd. north of the community of Pine Valley. The trail elevation ranges from 3,740 to 5,420 feet. Call for park maps & directions. **445-6235** *L*

Cleveland National Forest
79 Pacific Crest Indian Creek Trail · Descanso District
Leash required. This 4 mile trail connects the Cuyamaca Rancho State Park with the Laguna Mountain Recreation Area. The trail covers elevations ranging from 4,600 to 5,425 feet. Take

Places to Go 29

Sunrise Hwy. to the Penny Pines Trailhead. Call for park maps & directions. **445-6235** *L*

Cleveland National Forest
80 Pacific Crest Trail - Descanso District
Leash required. The trail traverses varied terrain and vegetation areas. It can be entered at several locations allowing hikers to choose the length of their hike. **445-6235** *L*

Cleveland National Forest
81 Pine Creek Wilderness Area - Descanso District
This area has 13,000 acres ranging in elevation from 2,000 feet in the south to 4,000 feet in the north. Leash required. Call for maps. **673-6180** *L*

Cleveland National Forest
82 Sunset Trail - Descanso District
Leash required. 4 miles beginning across the road from the Meadows Information Kiosk on Sunrise Hwy at the 19.1 mile marker. Beautiful meadow area that circles a small water reservoir. Call for park maps & directions. **445-6235** *L*

Cleveland National Forest
83 Wooded Hill Nature Trail - Descanso District
Leash required. 1.5 mile trail leads you up to one of the highest points (6,223 ft.) in the Recreation Area. This difficult climb it is not recommended for small children, out of shape pets or people with disabilities. Call for park maps & directions. **445-6236** *M*

El Cajon
84 Cottonwood
Leash required. Open grassy area. Take Jamacha Rd. south to Hillsdale east turn right on Donahue to park. Thomas Bros.1272, B5. **694-3049** *S*

El Cajon
85 Damon Lane
Leash required. 29 acre open space. Take Hwy 8 east to Avocado south, then east on Fuerte Dr. to Damon Lane south to park. Thomas Bros.1271, J3. **694-3049** *M*

El Cajon
86 Lake Jennings Regional Park
Leash required. Located 5 miles east of El Cajon. This park features camping, fishing and miles of trails. Dogs aren't allowed on the trails but, there are lots of open areas to run. East 21 miles on Hwy 8 to Lake Jennings Park Rd. then north 1 mile. Thomas Bros 1232, E2. **694-3049** *M*

Lakeside
87 Louis A. Stelzer Regional Park
Leash required in this 300 acre of park. Dogs are not permitted on trails. However, there are plenty of open non-trail areas to take your dog. From Hwy 8 go north on Hwy 67 to Mapleview St. Exit east for .5 miles to Ashwood St. turn left and go a two miles to park.. Thomas Bros. 1232, C1. **694-3049** *L*

Pet Pages

El Cajon
88 Mount Gower Open Space Preserve Hike
Plan about 2 hours to complete this easy 4 mile hike. Take Interstate 8 to Hwy 67 to Mapleview St. in Lakeside. Go east 3 miles to Ashwood St. Left to San Vicente Rd. Right to Gunn Stage Rd. Left 1.5 miles to the entrance. *M*

El Cajon
89 Nancy Jane
Leash required. Take Hwy 8 east to Greenfield Dr. South turn left on La Cresta Rd. to a couple miles turn right on Suncrest Blvd. to park. Thomas Bros.1252, H3. **694-3049** *S*

El Cajon
90 Noble Canyon National Recreation Trail Hike
This 10 mile trail through a canyon area with a creek will take about 6-7 hours to hike. Take Interstate 8 east to Pine Valley exit, go west on Old Highway past Pine Valley County Park turn right onto Pine Creek Rd. to marked trail. *L*

El Cajon
91 Old Ironside
Leash required. A beautiful oak-lined creek runs through this park. Take Hwy 8 east past El Cajon exit Alpine Blvd. go east to Arnold Wy. south, turn right on Harbison Canyon Rd. and follow a few miles to park. Thomas Bros.1253, D1. **694-3049** *S*

La Mesa
92 Avocado
Leash required. Trees and open grassy space. Take Hwy 94 to Avocado Blvd. go north to Fury Lane then right to park. Thomas Bros. map 1271, G4. **694-3049** *S*

La Mesa
93 Harry Griffen Park
Leashes required. There are 50 acres to explore as well as a jogging trail if your feeling energetic. I-8 to Grossmont Blvd. north to Murray Rd. right to Water north to Milden St. Thomas Bros. 1251, C6. **469-4128** *M*

La Mesa
94 Lake Murray
Leashes required. Paved and dirt paths to take around the lake. Dogs must stay 50 feet from water. Take I-8 to Lake Murray Blvd. North to Kiowa Dr. Go left to the park. Thomas Bros. 1250, E6. **668-2050** *M*

Lakeside
95 Cactus
Leash required. This park is just off Hwy. 67. Turn east on Mapleview then left on Ashwood to park. Thomas Bros. 1232, B2. **694-3054** *S*

Places to Go

Lakeside
96 Lindo Lake
Leash required. One of the few fresh water lakes in the county. Hwy 67 north from Hwy 8. exit Mapleview east to Maine go south to Lakeshore Dr. east to lake. Thomas Bros. 1232, B3. **694-3062** *S*

San Diego
97 Allied Gardens Community Park
6' Leash required. Located at Greenbrier Ave. and Glenroy St. Take Hwy 15 to Friars Rd. east to Mission Gorge Rd. east to Zion Ave. east. to park. Thomas Bros. 1250, A6. **235-1129** *S*

San Diego
98 Anza - Borrego Desert State Park
6' Leash required. Designated areas only. Open 24 hrs/day. Call to have a park map & information mailed to you. Be prepared for very warm conditions! Bring lots of water. Dogs not allowed on trails. Thomas Bros. 1098, F5. **767-5311** *L*

San Diego
99 Chollas Lake Park
6' Leash required. Open from 6:30 a.m. - 8 p.m. There are 60 acres of light hiking. Kids under 15 can fish here. College Dr. off College Ave. west of Hwy 94. Thomas Bros. 1270, C6. **527-7683** *S*

San Diego
100 City Heights Recreation Center
Leash required. Located at 44th and Wightman. Take Hwy 805 to El Cajon Blvd. east to 44th St. south to park. Thomas Bros. 1269, H5. **236-7314** *S*

San Diego
101 El Capitan
Leash required. Elevation varies from 600 to 3,300 feet. There are 5 miles of trails running through mixed chaparral in this 2,800 acre park. I-8 to Hwy 67 north. 5 miles to Mapleview. East .5 miles to Ashwood. 4 miles. Corner of Wildcat Canyon Rd. /Blue Sky Ranch Rd. **694-3044** *L*

San Diego
102 El Monte Regional Park
Leash required. Spectacular scenery in this 98 acre park. 21 miles east on Interstate 8 to Lake Jennings Park Rd. Go north 1.5 miles to El Monte Rd. then 6 miles east to entrance. Thomas Bros. 429, H4. **694-3049** *L*

San Diego
103 Encanto Community Park
Leash required. Located at Wunderlin Ave. and 65th St. Take Hwy 94 to Euclid Ave. south to Imperial Ave. east to 65th St. north to park. Thomas Bros. 1290, D2. **527-3411** *S*

Pet Pages

San Diego
104 Flinn Springs Regional Park
Leash required. 40 acre park with oak trees for shade and boulders to climb on. 21 miles east on interstate 8 to Lake Jennings Park Rd. on south side of the freeway, take Old Hwy 80 east one mile to park entrance. Thomas Bros. 1232, J4. **694-3049** *M*

San Diego
105 Golden Hill Community Park
Leash required. Located at Golf Course Dr. and Russ Blvd. Take Hwy 94 to 28th St. north to park. Thomas Bros. 1289, D2. **235-1138** *S*

San Diego
106 Laguna Mountain Recreation Area
Leashes required. Open 24 hours a day. Campsites are available. There are over 10,000 acres within Cleveland National Forest. One mile east of Pine Valley on Route S-1. **445-6235** *L*

San Diego
107 Lake Morena Regional Park
Leashes required. Campsites are available within this 3,200 acre park. Dogs are not allowed on trails. Near Campo. East on interstate 8 to Buckman Springs Rd. go south 4 miles to Oak Dr. then west 3 miles to Lake Morena Dr. turn right into entrance. Thomas Bros. 430, A7. **694-3049** *L*

San Diego
108 Martin Luther King Jr. Park
Leash required. Skyline Dr. and 65th St. Take Hwy 94 to Euclid Ave. south to Imperial Ave. east to 65th St. south to park. Thomas Bros. 1290, D5. **527-3415** *S*

San Diego
109 Mission Trails Regional Park
Leashes required. <u>Dogs are allowed on trails.</u> One trail leads to the Old Mission Dam Historical Site. Interstate 8 to Mission Gorge Rd. go northeast about 4 miles then left on Father Junipero Serra Trail. Thomas Bros. 1230, C6. **668-3275** *M*

San Diego
110 North Park Community Park
Leash required. Located at Idaho St. and Howard Ave. Take Hwy 805 to El Cajon Blvd. west to Idaho St. south to park. Thomas Bros. 1269, D4. **235-1152** *S*

San Diego
111 Paradise Hills Park/ Rec. Center
Leash required. Located at Potomac St. and Paradise Valley Rd. Take Hwy 805 south to Plaza Blvd. east to park. Thomas Bros. 1290, D6. **527-3419** *S*

Places to Go

San Diego
112 Pine Valley Regional Park
Leash required. Escape the heat under pine and oak trees. 17 lawn covered acres. Interstate 8 to Pine Valley exit, go north on Pine Valley Rd. to the park. Thomas Bros. 1237, B6. **694-3049** *S*

San Diego
113 Potrero Regional Park
Leash required. 115 acres for camping, picnicing and fun. East on Hwy 94 to Potrero then one mile north on Potrero Valley Rd. go east one mile to entrance. Thomas Bros. 1316, E7. **694-3049** *M*

San Diego
114 Skyline Community Park
Leash required. Skyline Dr. near Meadowbrook Dr. Take Hwy 94 east to Skyline south to park. Thomas Bros. 1290, H4. **527-3486** *S*

San Diego
115 Standley Community Park
Leash required. Governor Dr. between Stadium and Mercer St. Exit Hwy 52 at Genesee Ave. go north to Governor west to park. Thomas Bros. 1228, D5. **552-1652** *S*

San Diego
116 Sunset Trail
This park covers over 7 miles on the western rim plateau of the Laguna Mountains featuring beautiful views and many trails. Leashes required. Interstate 8 east to Sunrise Hwy (east of Alpine) go north about 20 miles to Meadows Information station parking area. *L*

San Diego
117 Sweetwater County Park
Leash required. Over 580 acres of open space with 8 miles of trails along the river. 10 miles southeast of San Diego take interstate 805 south to Bonita Rd. go east 4 miles to San Miguel Rd. then to the park on Summit Meadow Rd. Thomas Bros. 1291, A5. **694-3049** *L*

San Diego
118 Sweetwater River Trail
This 5 mile trail runs along a golf course and then heads up into the hills. Interstate 805 south to Bonita Rd. go east about 4 miles to where the road crosses a bridge over the Sweetwater River. Trail starts by the bridge. Park on side streets. *M*

San Diego
119 Vallecito Regional Park
Leash required. 71 acre park with campsites and picnic areas. East on Interstate 8 to Octillo north 30 miles on S-2 to park. Thomas Bros. 430, C2. **694-3049** *M*

Pet Pages

San Diego
120 Wooded Hill Nature Trail
1½ mile trail in the Laguna Mountains. You can see San Diego and Catalina on a clear day. I- 8 east to Sunrise Hwy (N) about 22 miles. Left on road to Wooded Hill Campground. *M*

Spring Valley
121 Eucalyptus
Leash required. 100 year old Eucalyptus trees, some of the oldest in the city. Take Hwy. 8 east to Hwy 125 south exit Lemon Ave. east to Bancroft Dr. south to park. Thomas Bros. 1271, B3. **694-3049** *S*

Spring Valley
122 Goodland Acres
Leash required. Take 94 east to Bancroft Dr. south to Troy St. to park. Thomas Bros.1271, A6. **694-3049** *S*

Spring Valley
123 Spring Valley Park
Leash required. Open grassy area. Take Hwy 94 east to Broadway to east to Sweetwater Rd. south to Jamacha Rd. right side of road. Thomas Bros. 1291, A3. **694-3049** *S*

San Diego
124 Cuyamaca Rancho State Park
This park boasts 25,000 acres of mountainous terrain with over 120 miles of hiking trails. 50 miles of fire roads. North end adjoins Lake Cuyamaca (no swimming) three mile trail around the lake. Hwy 79 between Hwy 78 and Interstate 8. Thomas Bros. 1196, A1. **765-0755** *L*

San Diego
125 Sea Port Village - Port District
6 ft. leash required. Southwest end of downtown on bay. Thomas Bros. 1288, J4. **686-6200** *S*

San Diego
126 Embarcadero (North & South) - Port District
6 ft. leash required. Southwest end of downtown on bay. Thomas Bros. 1288, J4. **686-6200** *S*

San Diego
127 Shelter Island
6 ft. leash required. Take Hwy 5 south to Laurel St. go west to Harbor Dr. to Rosecrans St. turn left to Shelter Island Dr. to park. Thomas Bros. 1288, C3. **686-6200** *S*

San Diego
128 Harbor Island
6 ft. leash required. Take Hwy 5 to Laurel St. exit. go west to Harbor Dr. turn left onto Harbor Island. Park is along waters edge. Thomas Bros. 1288, F2. **686-6200** *S*

Places to Go

San Diego
129 Crosby Street Park
6 ft. leash required. Take Hwy 5 south to Logan Ave. (exit before Coronado Bridge) turn left on Crosby St. to park. Thomas Bros. 1289, C5. **686-6200** *S*

San Diego
130 Spanish Landing
6 ft. leash required. Take Hwy 5 to Airport exit (Laurel St.) go west to Harbor Island. Stroll the sidewalk along Harbor Dr. Thomas Bros. 1288, F1. **686-6200** *S*

National City
131 Pepper Park
6 ft. leash required. Take Hwy 5 south to Civic Center exit, go west to Tidelands Ave. go south to park. Thomas Bros. 1309, G5. **686-6200** *S*

Chula Vista
132 Bayside Park
6 ft. leash required. Take Hwy 5 south to Palm Ave. go west to 9th St. go north to park. Thomas Bros. 1329, G6. **686-6200** *S*

Imperial Beach
133 Dunes Park
6 ft. leash required. Located between Donax & Daisy St. Thomas Bros. 1329, E7. **686-6200** *S*

Oceanside
134 Oceanside Harbor
Leash required. Take a stroll on 2 miles of sidewalk around the harbor. If you're hungry, there are several restaurants you and your companion can choose from. Take I-5 to Harbor Dr. West to the harbor. *M*

Solana Beach
135 San Elijo Lagoon Wildlife Reserve - West
Leash required. Almost 2 miles of hiking on the north end of Solana Beach. Take I-5 to Lomas Santa Fe Dr. go west to Rios Ave. turn right to trail. *M*

Solana Beach
136 San Elijo Lagoon Wildlife Reserve - East
Leash required. There are about 2 miles of hiking trails around a beautiful lagoon. Birdwatching is great here! Take I-5 to Lomas Santa Fe Dr. go east to Santa Helena then take a left. Go left on Santa Victoria and left onto Santa Carina. Go to end. *M*

Pet Pages

Del Mar
137 Crest Canyon
Leash required. A pretty canyon hike of about 2 miles from Del Mar Heights Rd. north to Racetrack View Dr. I-5 to Del Mar Heights Rd. west to Requerdo Dr. right. Park along the street. *M*

Mira Mesa
138 Los Penasquitos Canyon Preserve Hike - Lopez Canyon
Leash required. 4 miles of canyon trails. Take I-5 to Sorrento Valley Blvd. east 1 mile to parking lot. Trail begins on south side of road. *M*

San Diego
139 Fry Creek Trail - Palomar Mountain
Leash Required. Fun and easy 1.5 mile trail begins and ends at Fry Creek Campgrounds. Take I-15 to Hwy S6 to the Fry Creek Campground. Just north of the East Grade/South Grade intersection. *M*

Poway
140 Stoneridge Trail
Leash required. Pleasant walk on an established trail that runs along Espola Rd. past the Bernardo Winery. You may see others on horseback along this trail. Take I-15 to Poway Rd. east to Espola Rd. go north to Valle Verde Rd. to park. *M*

Poway
141 Green Valley Truck Trail
Leash required. Popular dirt road for dogs, bikes and horses that takes you to the top of Ramona Dam. About 5 miles round trip. Take I-15 to Rancho Bernardo Dr. east to the bend where the road turns into Espola Rd. trail is on the east side. *M*

San Diego
142 Rose Canyon
Leash required. This is a scenic 3 mile canyon hike in the Golden Triangle area.. Take I-5 to La Jolla Village Dr. east to Genesee Ave south on Decoro Street. Park here and walk to trail. *M*

San Diego
143 Sacatone Overlook
View the Salton Sea, Carrizon Gorge and a railroad trestle. A dirt road takes you about 2 miles to a point where all can be seen. Take I-8 to Hwy 94. Go south to old Hwy. 80 then east to McCain Valley Rd. Then to Sacatone Spring Rd. turn right onto the dirt road. *M*

3 Restaurants

The following is a listing of restaurants with outdoor seating that will allow well-behaved pets to dine with their owners. Now you can go to the park or beach and have lunch with your four-legged friend. Rather than leaving your pet in a car while you dine and dash to get back to the car, allow him to accompany you to the restaurant. This way you and your pet can sit and relax. You can enjoy your meal, and your pet can enjoy the opportunity to people-watch.

37A Restaurants

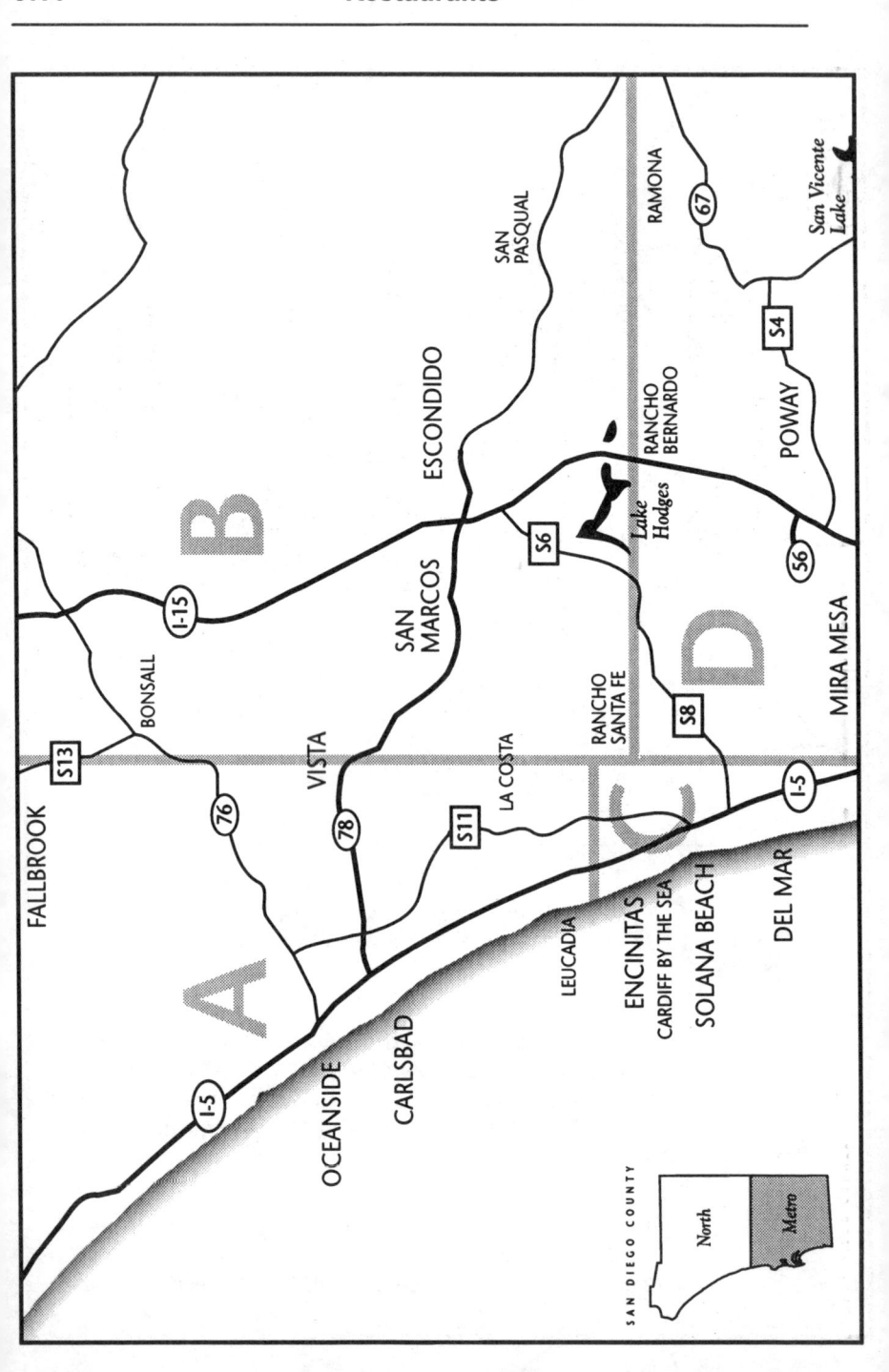

PetPages 37B

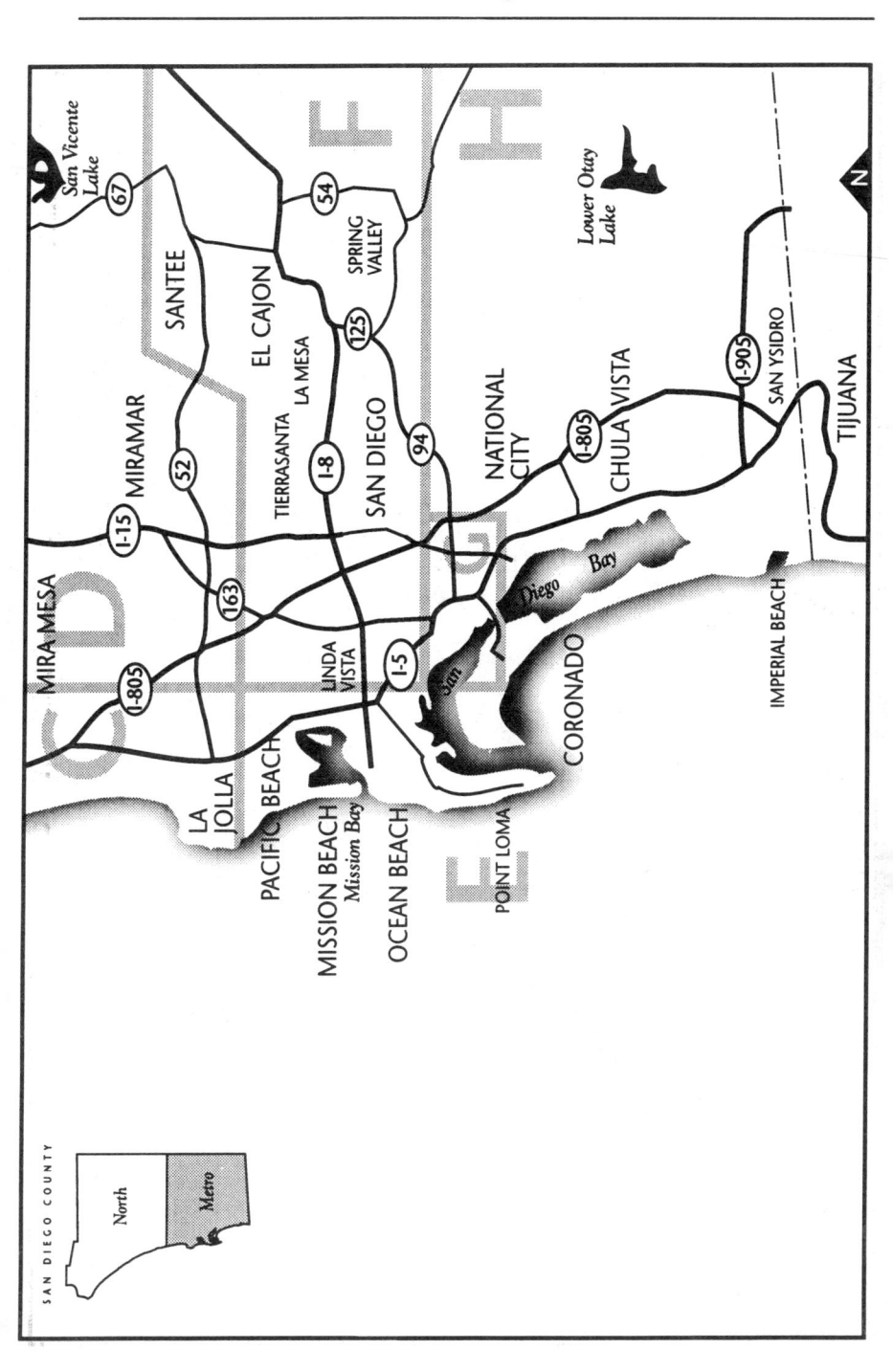

Pet Pages

Dining Tips

- Bring rawhide chew to occupy pet while you're dining.
- Only bring pets that will sit or lay quietly at the table.
- Pets should be well-mannered and not disturb other diners.
- Bring a water bowl for your pet; don't expect the restaurant to provide one.

For your convenience, restaurants that allow pets are listed by city. Other pet-friendly restaurants may exist in the county. Look for outside eating areas and ask the manager if they allow it. If it is not on our list, let us know and we'll include it in our next edition.

If you decide to dine at any of the listed restaurants, please let the management know how you found out about them. Management's awareness of pet owner visits will insure pet-friendly policies in the future.

MAP GRID A

1	ALBERTO'S MEXICAN FOOD 2952 Harding St	Carlsbad	434-3908
2	AMEDEO'S ITALIAN CAFE 2780 State St	Carlsbad	729-8799
3	ARMENIAN CAFE 3126 Carlsbad Blvd	Carlsbad	720-2233
4	CALDO POMODORO 2907 State St	Carlsbad	720-9998
5	CAMPUS CAFE 5966 La Place Ct # 150	Carlsbad	431-9210
6	CESSY TACO SHOP 3016 Carlsbad Blvd	Carlsbad	434-2648
7	DE VENNEY'S CARLSBAD CAFE 2943 State St.	Carlsbad	434-2500
8	DON'S COUNTRY KITCHEN 2885 Roosevelt St.	Carlsbad	729-2274
9	GRAND DELI 595 Grand Ave.	Carlsbad	729-4015
10	HENNESSEY'S TAVERN 2777 Roosevelt St.	Carlsbad	729-6951
11	JAY'S BOURMET PIZZA/SEAFOOD 2975 Carlsbad Blvd.	Carlsbad	720-9688
12	LA COSTA COFFE ROASTING CO. 6965 El Camino Real	Carlsbad	438-8160
13	MARIAH'S WEST WIND REST. 377 Carlsbad Blvd.	Carlsbad	729-6040
14	OVERSEAS RESTAURANT 2818 Roosevelt St.	Carlsbad	729-0348
15	PICK UP STIX CARLSBAD 2508 El Camino Real	Carlsbad	720-6252
16	PRIMO PIZZA & PASTA 7110 Avenida Encinas #103	Carlsbad	431-7155
17	SPIRITO'S RESTAURANT 300 Carlsbad Village Drive	Carlsbad	720-1132

Restaurants

MAP GRID A

#	Name	Address	City	Phone
18	TOGO'S	6971 El Camino Real	Carlsbad	431-5010
19	VILLAGE GRILLE	2833 State St.	Carlsbad	729-3601
20	AMEDEO'S ITALIAN CAFÉ	2780 State Street	Oceanside	729-8799
21	ARMENIAN CAFÉ	3126 Carlsbad Boulevard	Oceanside	720-2233
22	B B CAFE	1938 S Hill St	Oceanside	722-7337
23	BEACH BREAK CAFE	1902 S Hill St	Oceanside	439-6355
24	BEACH BREAK CAFÉ	1902 South Hill Street	Oceanside	439-6355
25	BUCCANEER GALLEY	1508 S Pacific St	Oceanside	439-8242
26	CHOPSTICK CHARLEY'S	2530 Vista Way	Oceanside	722-4000
27	DAVINA'S FINE MEXICAN	3320 Mission Ave	Oceanside	722-8017
28	HAMBURGER HEAVEN	714 N Hill St	Oceanside	722-2254
29	HARBOR FISH & CHIPS	276 Harbor Dr S # A	Oceanside	722-4877
30	HILL STREET COFFEE HOUSE	524 S Hill St	Oceanside	966-0985
31	JOHNNY MANANAS	308 Mission Ave	Oceanside	721-9999
32	MARY'S RESTAURANT	307 N Hill St # B	Oceanside	722-3052
33	SMOKEY'S BARBEQUE	608 Mission Ave	Oceanside	439-4763

MAP GRID B

#	Name	Address	City	Phone
34	BUBBA'S BAR-B-Q REST.	201 W Mission Ave	Escondido	745-9005
35	CAFE ARTISTA	427 N Escondido Blvd	Escondido	745-5461
36	CENTRE CITY CAFE	2680 S Escondido Blvd	Escondido	743-0291
37	CHAMPION'S FAMILY REST.	117 W Grand Ave	Escondido	747-0288
38	CHARLIE'S FAMILY RESTAURANT	210 N Ivy St	Escondido	738-1545
39	COCINA DEL CHARRO	525 N Quince St	Escondido	745-1382
40	DOMINGUEZ MEXICAN FOOD	311 W Mission Ave	Escondido	480-5565
41	ELIA'S RESTAURANT	1141 E Washington Ave	Escondido	741-2539
42	ITALIAN FEAST & PIZZERIA	330 W Felicita Ave	Escondido	739-0435
43	KOTIJA	663 N Broadway	Escondido	738-9447
44	METAPHOR CAFE & BISTRO	258 E 2nd Ave	Escondido	489-8890
	See our coupon			
45	THE METAPHOR	258 East Second Ave.	Escondido	489-8890
46	RICHARDSON'S DRIVE-IN	536 S Main St	Fallbrook	728-7754
47	WAYSIDE CAFE	507 S Main St # C	Fallbrook	723-9633
48	RAMONA CAFE	628 Main St	Ramona	789-8656
49	BUCKAROO BARBEQUE	1984 S Santa Fe Ave	Vista	727-8879
50	CASA LINDA	721 S Santa Fe Ave	Vista	726-3362
51	COYOTE CAFE	1450 N Santa Fe Ave	Vista	758-8724
52	CURBSIDE CAFE & BAKERY	307 E Vista Way	Vista	630-2747
53	OL' SMOKEY BBQ	750 Sycamore Ave	Vista	598-0048
54	PLUM DELI	2515 Pioneer Ave	Vista	598-3826
55	SANDWICH STOP	1850 Hacienda Dr	Vista	631-2710
56	SUNRISE CAFE	1250 S Santa Fe Ave	Vista	631-2812

MAP GRID C

#	Name	Address	City	Phone
57	HAMBURGER HULAS	102 Aberdeen Dr.	Cardiff	633-4852
58	LAS OLAS MEXICAN RESTAURANT	2655 S Highway 101	Cardiff	942-1860

MAP GRID C

#	Name	Address	City	Phone
59	MIRACLES CAFE	1953 San Elijo Ave	Cardiff	943-7924
60	N. COUNTY TACO AUCTIONEERS	1951 San Elijo Ave	Cardiff	942-8226
61	SAN SIMEON MEXICAN FOOD	2035 San Elijo Ave	Cardiff	944-0565
	See our coupon			
62	BAJA GRILL & CANTINA	1342 Camino Del Mar	Del Mar	792-6551
63	BOARD & BREW	1212 Camino Del Mar	Del Mar	481-1021
64	BOOMERANGS	526 Camino Del Mar	Del Mar	481-9111
65	CAFE CLASSICO	600 W Broadway St	Del Mar	234-8838
66	DEXTER'S DELI (MAINLY FOR DOGS!)	1231 Camino Del Mar	Del Mar	792-3707
67	DURANTE'S OF DEL MAR	2010 Jimmy Durante Blvd.	Del Mar	481-8312
68	ESMERALDA BOOKS & COFFEE	1555 Camino Del Mar	Del Mar	755-2707
69	GARDEN TASTE	1555 Camino Del Mar	Del Mar	730-1500
70	GREEK CUISINE CAFE	3860 Valley Center Dr	Del Mar	792-2233
71	JOHNNY ROCKETS	1555 Camino Del Mar	Del Mar	755-1954
72	KIRBY'S CAFE	215 15th St.	Del Mar	481-1001
73	MUCHO GUSTO MEXICAN GRILL	2668 Del Mar Heights Rd.	Del Mar	259-6855
74	OCEAN GRILL	1231 Camino Del Mar	Del Mar	793-8823
75	PAPACHINO'S RISTORANTE	2650 Via De La Valle	Del Mar	481-7171
76	PICK UP STIX DEL MAR	2710 Via De La Valle	Del Mar	259-7849
77	SAM'S PIZZA	2212 Carmel Valley Rd.	Del Mar	755-6778
78	STRATFORD COURT CAFE	1307 Stratford Ct.	Del Mar	792-7433
79	101 DINER	552 1st. St.	Encinitas	753-2123
80	ALBERTO'S MEXICAN FOOD	852 N. Highway 101	Encinitas	942-6231
81	ANGELO'S BURGERS	608 1st St.	Encinitas	943-9115
82	COLORS PIZZA CAFÉ	745 First Street	Encinitas	944-1447
83	ENCINITAS CAFE	531 1sr St.	Encinitas	632-0919
84	LA SALSA RESTAURANTF	219 N. El Camino Real	Encinitas	436-9266
85	OSCAR'S	1505 Encinitas Blvd.	Encinitas	632-0222
86	PAPA TONI'S PIZZA	232 N. Highway 101	Encinitas	944-6989
87	PAPA TONI'S PIZZA	554 Sante Fe Dr.	Encinitas	753-2885
88	POTATO SHACK CAFE	120 W. I St.	Encinitas	436-1282
	See our coupon			
89	ROXY RESTAURANT & ICE CREAM	517 1st St.	Encinitas	436-5001
90	SAKURA BANA	1031 First Street	Encinitas	942-6414
91	ST. GERMAINS CAFE	1010 1st St.	Encinitas	753-5411
92	TOMASO'S ITALIAN RISTORANTE	967 1st St.	Encinitas	632-1901
93	BALTIMORE BAGEL CO	4150 Regents Park Row	La Jolla	587-1136
94	BALTIMORE BAGEL CO	7523 Fay Ave # B	La Jolla	456-0716
95	BROTHERS RESTAURANT	4250 Executive Sq	La Jolla	452-3939
96	BULLY'S RESTAURANT	5755 La Jolla Blvd	La Jolla	459-2768
97	CAFE LAUTREC	7644 Girard Ave	La Jolla	459-9940
98	CASA LA JOLLA	828 Prospect Street	La Jolla	454-0859
99	CATALINA'S	8008 Girard Ave	La Jolla	454-2356
100	COFFEE CUP	1109 Wall St	La Jolla	454-2819
101	COFFEE HOUSE-NORTH SHORE	2161 Avenida De La Playa	La Jolla	456-2454
102	COME ON IN	1030 Torrey Pines Rd	La Jolla	551-1063
103	FROGLANDER'S YOGURT	915 Jpearl Street	La Jolla	459-3764
104	GIRARD GOURMET	7837 Girard Ave	La Jolla	454-3321
105	IL FORNO	909 Prospect Street	La Jolla	459-5010
106	LA JOLLA BREWING CO	7536 Fay Ave	La Jolla	456-2739

Restaurants

MAP GRID C

107	**LA JOLLA COFFEE STOP** 8867 Villa La Jolla Dr	La Jolla	558-0661
108	**LA JOLLA SPICE CO** 5737 La Jolla Blvd	La Jolla	456-2272
109	**LA TERRAZZA** 8008 Girard Ave	La Jolla	459-9750
110	**LIVING ROOM COFFEE HOUSE** 1010 Prospect St	La Jolla	459-1187
111	**MARKETPLACE GRILLE** 1030 Torrey Pines Rd	La Jolla	456-9576
112	**ON THE JUICE** 9500 Gilman Dr	La Jolla	558-7952
113	**PARADISE WALK** 7731 Fay Ave	La Jolla	551-0751
114	**PORTER'S STUDENT PUB** 9500 Gilman Dr	La Jolla	587-4828
115	**RICE BOWL** 6984 La Jolla Blvd	La Jolla	551-9685
116	**SAMMY'S CAL. WOODFIRED** 702 Pearl St	La Jolla	456-5222
117	**SECRET GARDEN COFFEE SHOP** 928 Silverado St	La Jolla	551-0928
118	**SHELBY'S** 6737 La Jolla Boulevard	La Jolla	456-6660
119	**SHELBY'S** 6737 La Jolla Blvd	La Jolla	456-6660
120	**STELLA BELLA COFFEE** 7417 La Jolla Blvd	La Jolla	551-9997
121	**THE LIVING ROOM** 1010 Prospect Street	La Jolla	459-1187
122	**BOLERO MEXICAN REST.** 6024 Paseo Delicias	Rancho Sf	756-5157
123	**CAFE MILLE FLEURS** 6009 Paseo Delicias	Rancho Sf	756-0773
124	**DELICIAS** 6106 Paseo Delicias	Rancho Sf	756-8000
125	**MILLE FLEURS RESTAURANT** 6009 Paseo Delicias Ave	Rancho Sf	756-3085
126	**CAFE 501** 437 S. Highway 101 #501	Solana Beach	792-1553
127	**CAFE EUROPA & DELI** 667 Rodolfo Dr.	Solana Beach	793-4693
128	**CALIFORNIA PIZZA KITCHEN** 437 S. Highway 101	Solana Beach	793-0999
129	**COAST CARBO STATION** 125 North Highway 101	Solana Beach	481-9800
130	**PIZZA PORT** 135 N. Highway 101	Solana Beach	481-7332
131	**RUBIO'S RESTAURANT** 437 S. Highway 101	Solana Beach	259-9611
132	**SUBWAY SANDWICHES & SALADS** 124 Lomas Santa Fe Dr.	Solana Beach	792-1158
133	**ZINC CAFE** 132 S. Cedros Ave	Solana Beach	793-5436
134	**DAILY'S RESTAURANT** 8915 Towne Centre Dr	Utc	453-1112

MAP GRID D

135	**ATHENS MARKET CAFE** 11640 Carmel Mountain Rd	Carmel Mtn.	675-2225
136	**GREEK CORNER CAFE** 11885 Carmel Mountain Rd	Carmel Mtn.	485-6207
137	**JUICE CLUB** 11738 Carmel Mountain Rd.	Carmel Mtn.	487-1500
138	**ACAPULCO MEXICAN REST.** 4060 Clairemont Mesa Blvd	Clairemont	483-9222
139	**DAPHNE'S GREEK CAFE** 13479 Poway Rd	Poway	679-8898
140	**EL COMAL MEXICAN REST.** 12845 Poway Rd	Poway	486-1010
141	**KENSINGTON COFFEE HOUSE** 13479 Poway Rd.	Poway	748-2887
142	**MEXICOCINA RESTAURANT** 12213 Poway Rd	Poway	748-6452
143	**NEVA'S CAFE** 13252 Poway Rd	Poway	748-2465
144	**PAPACHINOS RESTAURANT** 13425 Poway Rd	Poway	748-7100
145	**RALLY'S HAMBURGERS** 13230 Poway Rd	Poway	679-9035
146	**BERNARD'O RESTAURANT** 12457 Rancho Bernardo Rd	Rancho Bern	487-7171
147	**CHICKENETTE** 16719 Bernardo Center Dr	Rancho Bern	451-7808
148	**ELEPHANT BAR & RESTAURANT** 17051 W Bernardo Dr	Rancho Bern	487-7181
149	**ANITA'S MEXICAN SEAFOOD** 13211 Black Mountain Rd	Rancho Penasq	484-5789
150	**BUCKY'S OF BOSTON** 13215 Black Mountain Rd	Rancho Penasq	484-1132
151	**GREEK CORNER RESTAURANT** 13185 Black Mountain Rd	Rancho Penasq	484-9197
152	**CANYON GRILL** 9823 Carroll Canyon Rd # F	San Diego	271-4052

Pet Pages

MAP GRID D

153	GOURMET BAGGER REST.	7128 Miramar Rd	San Diego	689-2600
154	BEANZ	10425 Tierrasanta Blvd	Tierra	279-4704

MAP GRID E

155	BAY BOOKS CAFÉ	1029 Orange Ave	Coronado	435-0070
156	CAFÉ 1134	1134 Orange Ave	Coronado	437-1134
157	CECIL'S	1031 Orange Ave	Coronado	435-4660
158	DAIRY QUEEN	926 Orange Ave	Coronado	437-4183
159	DELI BY THE BAY	1201 First Street	Coronado	437-1006
160	FRESH-BAKED GOODIES	853 Orange Ave	Coronado	435-9272
161	KENSINGTON COFFEE HOUSE	1106 1st Street	Coronado	437-8506
162	MARCO'S ITALIAN RESTAURANT	1100 Orange Ave	Coronado	435-4161
163	PEOHE'S	1201 1st St # 3	Coronado	437-4474
164	PRIMAVERA PASTRY CAFÉ	956 Orange Ave	Coronado	435-4191
165	PRIMAVERA PASTRY CAFFE	956 Orange Ave	Coronado	435-4191
166	RHINOCEROS CAFE & GRILL	1166 Orange Ave	Coronado	435-2121
167	VIVA NOVA	1138 Orange Ave	Coronado	435-2124
168	DEMPSEY'S AT OCEAN BEACH	5119 1/2 Saratoga Ave	Ocean Bch	222-7740
	See our coupon			
169	ATOLL RESTAURANT	3999 Mission Blvd	Pacific Bch	539-8635
170	CAFE 976	976 Felspar St	Pacific Bch	272-0976
171	CAFE ATHENA	1846 Garnet Ave	Pacific Bch	274-1140
172	CAFE CREMA	1001 Garnet Ave	Pacific Bch	273-3558
173	EL INDIO MEXICAN REST.	4120 Mission Blvd	Pacific Bch	272-6985
174	GOOD TIME CHARLIE'S	910 Grand Ave # 101	Pacific Bch	274-3834
175	HEALTHY CHOICE	4475 Mission Blvd	Pacific Bch	483-3988
176	PB SEAFOOD	4535 Mission Blvd	Pacific Bch	483-5500
177	SLICE'N ICE	3146 Mission Boulevard	Pacific Bch	488-7760
178	BLUE FIN GRILL	3770 Hancock St # G	Point Loma	692-1410
179	CAFE 1018	1018 Rosecrans St	Point Loma	523-1018
180	GREEK CORNER CAFE	3615 Midway Dr	Point Loma	224-1450
181	GREEN BURRITO	3225 Sports Arena Blvd	Point Loma	523-2428
182	MARDI GRAS CAFE & MARKET	3185 Midway Dr # E	Point Loma	223-5501

MAP GRID F

183	BEEF 'N BUN WHISTLE STOP	2477 Fletcher Pky	El Cajon	465-0767
184	BOLL WEEVIL	335 N 2nd St	El Cajon	444-4438
185	CAJON PASS DELI	1195 N Cuyamaca St	El Cajon	562-1689
186	CASA SANCHIZ	1530 Jamacha Rd	El Cajon	444-7713
187	CONTRERAS TACO SHOP	2990 Jamacha Rd	El Cajon	660-8699
188	GAETANO'S RESTAURANT	820 Jamacha Rd	El Cajon	588-7838
189	KATIE MC GUIRE'S PIE & BAKE	2650 Jamacha Rd	El Cajon	670-0460
190	KIP'S CAFE	1058 E Main St	El Cajon	442-1211
191	KIP'S MANDARIN RESTAURANT	382 N 2nd St	El Cajon	442-1211
192	ON THE ROCKS	518 E Main St	El Cajon	579-3537
193	PAPACHINO'S RISTORANTE	627 Parkway Plz	El Cajon	593-8500

Restaurants 43

MAP GRID F

194	RUBIO'S RESTAURANTS 399 N Magnolia Ave	El Cajon	440-3325
195	CHILANGOS MEXICO CITY GRILL 142 University Ave	Hillcrest	294-8646
196	DAVID'S PLACE 3766 5th Ave	Hillcrest	294-8908
197	JUICE CLUB 510 Robinson Ave	Hillcrest	683-2582
198	DAIRY QUEEN 2000 Main St # 101	Julian	765-2839
199	JULIAN GRILLE 2224 Main St	Julian	765-0173
200	KENDALL'S KORNER 2603 B St	Julian	765-1560
201	MAMA'S ROYAL CAFE 2018 Main St	Julian	765-2039
202	ROMANO'S DODGE HOUSE 2718 B St	Julian	765-1003
203	BALTIMORE CAFE 5620 Baltimore Dr	La Mesa	698-1114
204	CARUSO'S 8201 La Mesa Boulevard	La Mesa	460-4800
205	CHARCOAL HOUSE RESTAURANT 9566 Murray Dr	La Mesa	465-7050
206	CHICKEN NEST 7200 Parkway Dr	La Mesa	589-0088
207	EUROPEAN GOURMET DELI 6126 Lake Murray Blvd	La Mesa	697-4848
208	GIOVANNI'S CAFE ITALIANO 5575 Baltimore Dr	La Mesa	461-7000
209	GOLD STAR TACO SHOP 5416 Lake Murray Blvd	La Mesa	463-8709
210	POR FAVOR MEXICAN REST. 8302 La Mesa Boulevard	La Mesa	698 5950
211	POR FAVOR MEXICAN REST. 8302 La Mesa Blvd	La Mesa	698-5950
212	RITA'S MEXICAN FOOD 7102 University Ave	La Mesa	466-0131
213	SALAZAR'S TACO SHOP 5660 Lake Murray Blvd	La Mesa	462-5031
214	ANNIE OAKLEY'S 12212 Woodside Ave	Lakeside	561-0798
215	LA PALAPA MEXICAN REST. 12169 Woodside Ave	Lakeside	561-8106
216	MAIN STREET CAFE 9930 Maine Ave	Lakeside	390-1178
217	SOMBRERO MEXICAN FOOD 12346 Woodside Ave	Lakeside	390-8350
218	VICTOR'S MEXICAN FOOD 12510 Lakeshore Dr	Lakeside	561-8873
219	CHARLEY'S FAMOUS HAMBURGERS 8213 Broadway	Lemon Grove	460-2690
220	EL INDIO SHOP 3695 India St	Mission Hills	299-0333
221	MISSION HILLS CAFE 808 W Washington St	Mission Hills	296-8010
222	ANTIQUE ROW CAFE 3002 Adams Ave	Normal Hghts	282-9750
223	AZTEC CAFE 6557 El Cajon Blvd	San Diego	583-2722
224	BIG KITCHEN 3003 Grape St	San Diego	234-5789
225	CAFE AMERICAS 4644 College Ave	San Diego	265-0022
226	CANORA'S INDIA ST. SANDWICH 3715 India St	San Diego	291-5938
227	CLASSIC BURGERS & SUBS 5157 College Ave	San Diego	582-3377
228	ESPRESSO ROMA COLLEGE AVE 5131 College Ave	San Diego	229-1239
229	EVA'S COCINA & CANTINA 6690 Mission Gorge Rd	San Diego	284-5874
230	GOURMET BAGGER 1400 Camino De La Reina # 108	San Diego	299-1246
231	GRANGER'S CAFE 2432 El Cajon Blvd	San Diego	295-3735
232	GRANITE RIDGE CAFE 9655 Granite Ridge Dr	San Diego	467-9112
233	GREEK GARDENS GETAWAY 4334 54th St	San Diego	229-8888
234	KENSINGTON COFFEE HOUSE 4141 Adams Ave.	San Diego	280-5153

MAP GRID G

235	ALIZE RESTAURANT 777 Front St	Downtown	234-0411
236	AMELIA'S MEXICAN FOOD 245 7th Ave	Downtown	239-3934
237	ASAGGIO PIZZA PASTA PLUS 809 W Harbor Dr	Downtown	234-2407
238	ASTI RISTORANTE 728 5th Ave	Downtown	232-8844

MAP GRID G

239	ATHENS MARKET TAVERNA	109 W F St	Downtown	234-1955
240	BARNETTS GRAND CAFE	601 Pacific Hwy	Downtown	544-1122
241	BAY CAFE	1050 N Harbor Dr	Downtown	595-1083
242	BIG MAMA & CO EATERY	1963 India St	Downtown	235-6262
243	BISTRO 2000	428 C St	Downtown	231-6620
244	CAFE 222	222 Island Ave	Downtown	236-9902
245	CAFFE ITALIA	1704 India St	Downtown	234-6767
246	CASABLANCA CAFE	813 6th Ave	Downtown	238-1330
247	CERVECERIA SANTA FE	600 W Broadway	Downtown	696-0043
248	COTTAGE CAFE	2321 5th Ave	Downtown	696-0071
249	EL INDIO SHOP	409 F St	Downtown	239-8151
250	GREEK ISLANDS CAFE	879 W Harbor Dr	Downtown	239-5216
251	K-9 COUNTRY CLUB	202 C St	Downtown	239-0304
252	KABOB HOUSE	1125 6th Ave	Downtown	231-1969
253	CHEESE SHOP	401 G Street	San Diego	232-2303
254	TRATTORIA LA STRADA	702 Fifth Ave	San Diego	239-3400

MAP GRID H

255	TOMATOES PLUS	4346 Bonita Rd	Bonita	479-8494
256	BEAN POT'S DELI	945 Otay Lakes Rd	Chula Vista	421-8639
257	GALLEY AT THE MARINA	550 Marina Parkway	Chula Vista	422-5714
	See our coupon			
258	JIMMY'S FAMILY RESTAURANT	1198 3rd Ave	Chula Vista	427-7161
259	LA SALSA RESTAURANT	295 E Orange Ave	Chula Vista	426-3850
260	MARISCO'S MAZATLAN	1287 3rd Ave	Chula Vista	422-3311
261	PAPA DAVE'S VILLAGE WEST	247 3rd Ave	Chula Vista	498-1847
262	PARISI'S ITALIAN RESTAURANT	323 Broadway	Chula Vista	420-4490
	See our coupon			
263	POOR GOURMET	388 F St	Chula Vista	691-9646
264	RAFA'S TACO SHOP	1550 Broadway	Chula Vista	476-1290
265	THE DUCHESS COFFEE HOUSE, DELI	247 3rd Ave.	Chula Vista	498-1847
	See our coupon			
266	WOODY'S DOCKSIDE REST.	550 Marina Pky	Chula Vista	422-5714
267	BRENDORY'S	710 Seacoast Dr	Imperial Bch	423-3991
268	EL TAPATIO MEXICAN FOOD	260 Palm Ave	Imperial Bch	423-3443
269	MRS T'S PIZZA	807 Seacoast Dr	Imperial Bch	423-4444
270	MY LITTLE CAFE	809 Seacoast Dr	Imperial Bch	429-6378

Exercise & Play

4 Exercise & Play

To keep your pet happy and healthy, daily exercise and play is a must. Being active with your pet is good for both of you. This is your time to bond, relax, exercise, and have fun with your pet on a daily basis. Pick an activity that you both can enjoy. This time with you will become the highlight of your pet's day. Pets are reliable and enthusiastic playmates. Unlike most people, he'll look forward to your exercise routine.

Without a daily exercise routine, pets become bored and that's when trouble begins. Your pet will look for something to occupy his time and mind. For dogs, this may end up being barking, digging, chewing, or finding ways to escape. A bored cat may scratch, climb, or yowl.

The type and amount of exercise will depend on you and your pet's interest, age, and health. You and your pet should enjoy the activity. Don't force a pet to participate in something he clearly doesn't like. Talk with your veterinarian about your pet's health with respect to an exercise plan. This is especially important for aging or overweight pets.

Just like aerobics, begin your exercise routine with an easy warm up and end with a cool down. If possible, try to set aside the same time every day for your pet; they love routine. Avoid exercising one hour before or after meals.

Begin exercise slowly. Keep an eye on your pet and be prepared to stop if he appears tired or out of breath. He may slow down, pant heavily, or even refuse to move. He's telling you — STOP, I'm pooped! Don't overdo it. Pets will experience sore, stiff muscles too.

If you'll be exercising in the evening when it's dark, be sure that you and your pet are visible. Reflective collars and vests are available for pets.

What to do when you can't be there . . .

There will be times when, for whatever reason, you won't be able to do your daily exercise with your pet and that's okay. Just plan for someone else to fill in for you. This may be a neighbor, friend, pet sitter, or even pet daycare. Your pet will miss you, but will be appreciative of the ongoing routine and care.

Exercise & Play

Pet sitters are available to do daily stops at your home to walk, play, or feed your pet. This is wonderful for times when you're not feeling well, tied up at work, or simply unable to exercise your pet.

Another alternative is pet daycare. This is now available in many cities. Owners drop their pets off for a day filled with fun and companionship. Depending on the daycare center, it may offer swimming, indoor and/or outdoor play, scheduled exercise time, and rest. Some centers even offer obedience training. Use the same care as selecting any petcare: Visit and ask questions.

Playmates

The next best playmate is another dog or cat for your pet to play with when you're unavailable. Pets with partners are happier, healthier, and live longer. A playmate helps lighten the owner's load. Two can play, groom, rest, and explore. It brings new life to the current pet. If adding another pet just isn't possible, consider a plan where your pet can get together with a compatible pet friend. This may mean that you drop Fifi off at your friend's house to play with her friend Skippy.

Indoor and Outdoor Pets

Being left alone for eight to ten hours each day can get lonely for a pet. And, boredom usually spells trouble. Create diversions: Leave your pet with entertaining toys. When you're home, make sure your pet gets plenty of play and exercise with you.

Tips for Indoor Pets

- Establish a regular routine for morning and evening.

- Include exercise in daily schedule.
- Spend quality time with your pet.
- Make sure area where you're leaving pet is safe.
- Help make home comfortable for your pet; provide a comfortable bed, leave a radio or TV on to keep pet company, and don't forget safe toys.
- For dogs, hire a dog-walking service — or a dog-loving neighbor — to break up your dog's day with a visit and some exercise.
- Adopt a second pet.
- Give your pet an interesting outdoor view. (Pets like to watch activity: squirrels, birds, people, etc.)
- Phone home and leave messages for pets.
- For dogs, limit crate time to three or four hours a day (except at bedtime).
- Don't make a big deal over departures and arrivals.

Tips for Outside Dogs

Dogs can live outside, but are happiest when they're inside with their pack (you). If you have an outdoor dog, he can be eased into the indoor life with proper training.

Don't expel a dog to the outside because of a problem behavior. Instead, get proper training for your pet. Most problems stem from boredom. Your dog will be just as bored in the yard as he was in the house, therefore now you risk having greater problems than you already do.

If your dog enjoys his freedom and it works with your lifestyle, keep him an outward hound. But keep him healthy and happy by providing proper shelter and family interaction. Your dog should have a shaded area, shelter, fresh water, plenty of exercise, and playtime with you. Make sure your yard has no escape routes or dangerous objects. Be prepared to relocate your pet indoors when weather is extreme.

Dog Exercise

Begin any exercise program slowly and gradually increase the duration or difficulty. Be sensitive to the weather for outdoor activities. Avoid activities in extreme weather. During hot months, plan exercise in early or late day when it's cooler. Always have plenty of water available and take breaks. And don't forget pet sunscreen for light-colored pets. Their sensitive noses and ears will burn on sunny days.

Exercise with your dog will be safer and much more enjoyable, if your pet is obedience trained. It's not fun to walk a dog who's pulling you down the street. It will be important that your pet know the basics like sit, stay, come, and heel.

Walking

There isn't a dog who doesn't enjoy a walk with his best friend. However, for you to share the enjoyment, your pet must know how to heel (walk at your side with no pulling on the leash). If he doesn't know how to heel, this would be a good time to incorporate a little training into the walk. A brisk twenty-minute walk two times a day will satisfy most pet's exercise needs.

Jogging

Although jogging may be your chosen form of exercise, it may or may not be a good choice for your pet. Talk with your veterinarian before jogging; it is not recommended for small breeds, aging pets, or pets with joint problems. Never force a dog to run.

Exercise caution on warm days. Hot or rough surfaces can cause blisters or cracked pads. Be sure to check your pet's paws frequently and have plenty of fresh water available for him.

Biking with dog

This is one of the most strenuous activities for a dog because it requires him to maintain a constant pace to keep up with you. To insure that your pet is biking material, check with your veterinarian before beginning a biking program. Bike at a speed that allows your dog to trot rather than run. Check your pet's paws frequently for blisters or cracked pads. Avoid biking with your pet on hot days. Stop for water breaks.

Swimming

Some dogs absolutely love to swim and there are others that are less than thrilled at the thought of getting wet. Swimming is gentler on joints, which can be good for aging pets or pets with joint problems. DO NOT ASSUME ALL DOGS KNOW HOW TO SWIM. Be prepared to assist if your pet seems unsure. With some support and encouragement from you, a willing pet will quickly catch on. For those pets that will fetch, throwing a tennis ball or any other floatable toy out in the water is great fun and exercise. Watch for any signs of fatigue. Dogs can drown from exhaustion. Be sure that your pet has a safe path into the water. Slippery rocks, broken glass, fallen branches, or other sharp objects in or around water's edge can be extremely hazardous. Discourage pet from drinking water found in lakes, streams, and salt water. Parasites and bacteria found in these bodies of water can be harmful. Instead, bring fresh water from home for your pet to drink.

Pool Proof Your Dog

If your dog has access to a swimming pool, make

sure she has an easy way out such as steps or a slanted board. Bring your dog in the pool and show her how to get out. Again, do not assume that she will figure it out on her own.

For pets that are less sure of the water, there are life vests. These are especially good for boaters who take their pets.

Fetch or Catch

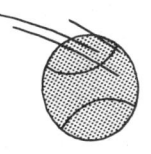

A game of fetch is great for owners who want to relax while their pet exercises. This activity assumes that your pet has been taught to return the thrown object. Some pets will automatically retrieve the object with little training. Most pets will probably require some training. Once trained, this is an excellent outlet for energy and dogs love it. Experiment with your pet to figure out what is his favorite item to fetch or catch. Some favorites include tennis balls, Kongs™ (beehive shaped rubber toy that bounces erratically when thrown), sticks, and Frisbees™. For long distance throws, use a tennis racket to hit the tennis ball. Always play on soft grassy areas. Asphalt or concrete can be hard on a pet's feet.

Dog Play

Okay, so your pet is exercised and rested. Now it's time for fun. Playtime for your pet may or may not include you. His preference would be to have you participate. But for those times you aren't there to play, provide your pet with toys and activities that will keep him occupied. The bottom line is to have fun, be creative, and get silly with your pet. Trust me, he'll love it!

Outdoor Pets

Liven up a boring backyard by creating a playground

for your pet. Think about your pet and what he'd like to do during the day. If he's a digger, put in a sandbox for him. Bury some of his favorite toys in the sand. If your yard is somewhat secluded, maybe a ramp leading up to a perch with a view would satisfy his curiosity and allow him to see activity outside his yard. Or, a cutout in the fence that would allow a view but no escapes or biting passersby. A tire (no steel belt tires) hanging from a tree may be a good chew or tug toy for a large dog. Is your dog a leaper or jumper? Then maybe a series of hurdles could prepare him for agility competition. Even a large empty box could provide hours of entertainment. Invite another dog friend to spend the day. Encourage your pet to use his hunting skills by hiding treats or toys in the yard.

Dog Play Groups

For a really special treat, get your pet together with a number of his other canine pals for some free play. The meeting can take place at a home with a yard or a public area that preferably allows pets off leash. Doing this on a regular basis is a lot of fun for the dogs and spectators. The dogs will form friendships with each other and will really look forward to the group session. Be prepared for an enthusiastic display of play skills as they race, chase, roll, tumble, jump, and bark. Be mindful of toy possessiveness. It may be better not to bring toys if they tend to fight over them. Or, bring enough so that the fighters each have one. Guaranteed, you will leave with one happy pup.

Hide and Seek

Remember how much fun you used to have playing hide and seek? Well, now you can relive childhood memories with your four legged kid(s) and have just as much fun today. Simply put your pet in a "sit-stay" and head for a hiding place. Then give your pet the "okay" signal to look for you. Lavish your pet with praise when she finds you. Start off with easy hiding spots so that your pet gets the hang of the game. This can be played inside or outside. Another twist is to hide treats or special toys and let your pet find them. Be sure to vary the pattern so it's a challenge.

Tracking

For dogs that like to use their noses, tracking is lots of fun. Begin by putting your pet in "sit-stay" away from the tracking area. She may watch from a distance. Then take a treat your pet likes (cheese or hot-dogs work well), rub a little on your shoes, and scuff a path through the grass. Periodically drop a little piece of the treat along the path. Go back and take your pet to the start of the laid track, and encourage her to follow the track. Using her nose, she'll follow the track and collect the treat rewards along the way. As she becomes better, the track can become longer and more erratic.

Homemade Toys

Some of the best toys come from the grocery store. Empty paper grocery bags, cardboard tubes from paper towels or giftwrap (especially after you shout the ta-dooo, ta-dooo rebel yell through them), and empty plastic milk containers. Granted, these are short-lived "toys" but, for that brief moment your pet will be captivated by the excitement of something new and different. Basically, if you begin the play and show an interest in whatever the toy, your pet will want to be involved. No self-respecting pet turns down an opportunity to play.

Toys

There are wide varieties of toys available for dogs. As with children's toys, keep safety in mind as you purchase toys for your pet. So, let's say you've bought a large assortment of toys. They're scattered all over your home and your pet seems totally bored with all of them. What can you do? Add some interest back into these current toys. First, pick them all up and put them in a basket or box. As you do this, undoubtedly your pet will wonder what you're doing and where you're going with his possessions. Already his toys are taking on new meaning. Next, allow your pet to select one or two toys from the container. Each day put back the toys and allow him to select his toys for the day. This rotation of toys will help minimize toy boredom. Another important part of this process is your handling of the toys. If you're paying attention to his toys, then so will he. Pets like toys that have their owner's scent on them.

Another option is to take sterilized dog bones, Kongs™, or Nylabones™ (with holes drilled in them) and stuff them with a favorite treat like peanut butter or cheese. Your dog will spend hours chewing on these tasty toys.

Dog Tricks

Teaching a dog tricks can be enjoyable for pet and owner. Pets love to please their owner. Training a pet to learn new tricks requires patience, consistency, and rewards. Think about what new fun trick you can teach your pet. Whether it's shaking paws, fetching the newspaper, or barking on command, remember to have fun; this is play time.

Exercise & Play

Special Report From Barkin' Bailey

Our roving reporter, Barkin' Bailey, comes to us from a local park, where she's talking with fellow canines about their favorite activities.

Well Bailey . . .

"HELLO EVERYONE!!! Barkin' Bailey here. I put my nose to the ground to find out **what makes a dog's tail stand up in excitement.**

"**Playing** with our two-legged companions: Tag, exploring, hide & seek, tug, wrestling (carefully, so no one gets hurt).

"There are many pleasures in life that are treasured by dogs. Most involve their owners. I had an opportunity to interview a few lucky pooches here at the park. Here's what they had to say . . .

"Taylor, a golden retriever mix, explains indoor hide and seek: *It's silly, but it's so much fun. I sit while my companion hides. When I hear a tiny 'O.K.!' I'm off to find the secret hiding spot. This is where my keen senses are challenged. My ears listen for movement or breathing, my eyes are quick to see the sight of my friend, and my nose — oh, how I sniff and sniff. Sometimes I can find the secret hiding place only using my sense of smell. (NO, my friend is not stinky! I just know her scent.) When I find her, we jump and shout and run around. Sometimes this turns into a fun game of tag. We get all excited and woofy. Ohhh, I get all giggly, wiggly just thinking about it.*

"**Playing with other dogs** - YEAH!! Bowie, a park regular, enjoys the chance to meet and play with other dogs of all sizes, shapes and breeds. (Although, Bowie has been known to borrow toys from other dogs.)

"Relaxing with a friend. Thor, a sensitive German Shepherd, says his favorite activity is the quiet time spent with his owner and friend Chris. Thor's voice, filling with love and contentment, says, *Those quiet moments really make a difference. To a dog, nothing is more important than being with the pack.*

"Dining out. An athletic Old Danish Pointer, Bomber, joyfully states, *I'd go everywhere if I could! Lately I've even enjoyed going to restaurants around the area. I try to be very good and lay by the table, but sometimes I get excited with all the sights, smells, and sounds. One time the chef gave me a special treat. It was delicious!*

"Walks!!! Morning, noon, or night — anytime is right. Most all dogs prefer several frequent walks a day, although even one long hike is nice.

"A thorough and **gentle massage** and brushing session . . . sigh. Sam, a particularly active dog, says, *It's great for getting rid of stress.*

"A game of chase! Balls, Frisbees, cats, cars . . . oops . . . the last two are forbidden, but some dogs get carried away when they are not given any direction or toys to play with. It is also advisable to make sure it is a safe area to run openly. Some dogs say they even bring them back to be thrown again (humans call it retrieving).

"Lastly, but most importantly — **communication**. Everyone polled agrees that this is the hardest to establish, but that it makes such a difference in their relationships with humans. Max, a beautiful Rottweiler, says, *Humans just don't know dog language and theirs is so complicated! Sometimes it sounds like blah blah blah, Max, blah, blah, blah. But with consistent repetition, my companion now understands my communication for a walk, going out to do duties, dinner, snacks, playtime, and Alert — stranger approaching. In turn, I can proudly say my human vocabulary is up to 27 words. We get along so well when we understand each*

Exercise & Play 57

other. This is strongly encouraged for everyone!

"There are differences in choices of activities when you bring age into the equation. Puppies all want the same things — eat, play, bite everything (they're teething), and sleep. This pattern is repeated over and over, day and night.

"On the other hand, senior dogs usually voice an opinion for slower paced activities. A great idea comes from Muffin, a distinguished older terrier. She enjoys elderly neighbors and nursing homes. These folks are gentle with her, and they like to talk to her and pet her. Little kids are just too frisky and unpredictable for her to keep up with; she has gotten hurt in the past. Besides, Muffin says it does so much for the people. She's heard it said that dogs have been known to give joy and purpose to people's lives, and they actually live longer.

"When breed and personality are considered, there are so many more activities that are loved by some and others would just as soon pass by. Water is a good example of this. Some dogs just do not like water — especially baths. Others heard the word water and ears shot up A very rambunctious brown Labrador, Dakota, LOVES the water. He'll happily participate in boating, swimming, fetching sticks thrown in the water, running on the shore, playing in a child's pool, or even playing in the sprinklers. All this talk about playing in the water left a lot of tails wagging.

"Just like people, dogs have their own personality, likes, and dislikes. Some dogs are real outdoorsy, you know — frontier dogs. They like to hike, camp, travel, and explore. Then there are the couch potatoes who prefer the comfort and predictability of home. You'll find them relaxing in their favorite spot.

"Clubs like hunting, tracking, agility, Frisbee, and trail were mentioned. There are so many clubs and new ones are forming all the time. What's so great is how much fun these groups are! Try one and see. If it doesn't thrill you, try another club. The dogs who were members couldn't say enough good things about them.

"That's about it here at the park! Companions, please use this as a reference to get started with 'dog friendly' activities. Customize it for both you and your dog's pleasure. If you come up with a great tail wagging idea, please write the editors of this book and they may be able to print it in a future publication.

"Signing off, this is Barkin' Bailey, for the PetPages™."

Cat Play

Yes, cats are pretty independent and generally don't require a lot of our attention. But they really do like to play, some just may not realize it. Playtime is especially important for indoor cats. An outdoor cat has opportunities all day to hunt and play.

Playtime for a cat is just another form of hunting. You may notice that your cat has a ground or air hunt preference. If so, then your task is to think like a bird or mouse.

Cat Play Rules

1) Cats only play when they want to play. You can try coaxing them, but don't be disappointed if she doesn't go for it.

2) Cats have short attention spans. Play time will probably last 10 to 20 minutes.

3) Beware of very fast and sharp claws that may accidentally catch you.

4) Never leave string, yarn, or thread out unattended. Cats can become entangled in it and harm themselves. Also, it is very dangerous if the string

Exercise & Play

is ingested; the barbs on a cat's tongues do not allow it to spit the string out.

Hide & Seek

This is not for everyone. But, there are some unique kitties out there that really do participate in a rollicking game of hide and seek. You run and hide, kitty chases, and you pop out from your hiding spot as she careens closer. This is fast-paced. She won't be waiting for you to carefully select your hiding place. She'll be hot on your trail as you scurry around the corner. So you've got to be fast.

Chase me, Chase Me

Every now and then your cat may enjoy a good chase, that is, you chasing her — much like how littermates would chase each other about the room. A little squeal or "boo" sound-effect is optional as you almost catch her. The objective is to get close, but not catch her. Let her be the victor.

Catch the Light

In a dimly lit area, turn on flashlight and watch kitty try to catch the light as it moves around the room. You may want to begin this game with a pencil flashlight.

Toys

Think of safety first. No toys with loose, sharp parts that may poke, cut, or be swallowed.

Fishing

Another cat favorite looks similar to a fishing pole with a string and feathers attached on the end. This works well as a high flyin' bird or when darted along the floor.

Paper

Be creative and think paper. Cats love little paper balls to bat around the floor. They like piles of newspapers spread out and tented up. Biting corners of envelopes is another pastime. Empty paper grocery bags laid on their side always offers some mystery to a cat. This is especially true if she hears something gently tapping on the side of that bag (just don't let her know it's you). Moving paper or still, wherever there is paper, there will mostly likely be a cat sitting in the midst of it.

Boxes

Empty boxes capture the attention and curiosity of most cats. Tossing a small ball or cork in the box will add further interest to a cat. After the mystery of the box is solved, you'll probably find your cat happily catching a nap in the new "hiding" place.

Bunny Kick Toys

Once a cat catches its prey, it will roll over on its back while holding its prey against its stomach and bunny kick it. Your cat may enjoy bunny kicking a tennis ball, a stuffed sock (particularly if it's stuffed with catnip), or any small soft stuffed object the size of a mouse or bird.

Ball Games

Another spin on the hunt game for kitty is to roll any small object for her to chase. The key here is to roll the object away from her, not toward her. The game is to think like an itty-bitty mouse running and hiding from your big, scary cat. Proven rollable objects that have met cats' expectations are ping-pong balls, plastic golf balls, empty plastic thread spools, small plastic egg-shaped containers, plastic lemons,

Exercise & Play 61

rollable nuts, and wine corks.

Movie Matinees

Yes, there are cats that enjoy a good video. There are even videos on the market that are specifically made for cats. Try it, see if your cat isn't mesmerized. No popcorn necessary. This is a great thing to leave on for kitty when she's alone.

Catnip

Catnip, the recreational drug for cats, can be grown or purchased in pet stores. The fresher the better. Intoxicated cats may become mellow, sleepy, playful, feisty, or content. Many toys are available with catnip. They will need to be replaced periodically as they lose their "nip" appeal.

Playground

Provide your cat with a "playground." This may include objects to climb, scratch, high places to hide, or catwalks. These can be purchased or made.

Let The Sun Shine In

Naps in the sun are vital to cats happiness. A sunny window view is ideal. Place a chair or table in front of the window so that kitty can enjoy her nap site. Window sill mounts are also available to accommodate cat perches. Never leave windows open without screens, cats can fall out.

Pet Pages

5 Clubs & Activities

Take your pick — are you interested in a cat group or a dog group? Purebred or mixed — active or show? Whatever your interest, there's bound to be a group just for you. This section lists a national contact for each activity. This contact may be used as a resource to locate local clubs in your area. There is also a list of local clubs in the DIRECTORY section. If you do not see the club you're looking for, please call the national contact for more information.

Dog Clubs & Activities

Dog Shows (Breed Shows)

The purpose of dog shows is to evaluate purebred, registered dogs as to how well they compare with written breed standards. The standards Include size, color, temperament, proportion, structure, and movement. In essence, they are looking for the ideal dog to represent that breed. Spayed or neutered pets are not allowed

For more information, contact the following clubs.

American Kennel Club
5580 Centerview Drive
Suite 200
Raleigh, NC 27606
919-233-9767

United Kennel Club
100 East Kilgore Road
Kalamazoo, MI 49001-5598
616-343-9020

Obedience Trials

Obedience trials test a dog's ability to perform a set of exercises. The dog's appearance is not judged. Exercises that are judged include the ability to heel on-lead and off-lead, stand for examination, come when called, sit and lie down on command. Advanced exercises include jump and retrieve on-command, ability to read hand signals, and recognize handler's scent on articles.

Contact the following clubs for more information regarding obedience trails.

Clubs & Activities

American Kennel Club
5580 Centerview Drive
Suite 200
Raleigh, NC 27606
919-233-9767

United Kennel Club
100 East Kilgore Road
Kalamazoo, MI 49001-5598
616-343-9020

AKC Junior Showmanship

Junior Showmanship is for young handlers between the ages of 10 and 18 years old. They are judged on their handling abilities and skills. The dog is not judged.

Contact AKC for more information.

American Kennel Club
5580 Centerview Drive
Suite 200
Raleigh, NC 27606
919-233-9767

AKC Canine Good Citizen Test

This test is open to pure and mixed breed dogs. The purpose is to demonstrate that the pet has good manners. Each dog is judged individually on a set of ten exercises; it is not competitive. The pet receives a certificate for passing the test. Below is the list of exercises required in the CGC test.

1) Appearance and grooming.

2) Accepting a friendly stranger.

3) Walk on a loose lead.

4) Walk through a crowd.

5) Sit politely for petting.

Pet Pages

6) Sit down on command/stay in place.

7) Come when called.

8) Reaction to another dog.

9) Reaction to distractions.

10) Dog left alone.

Any group, club, or dog enthusiast may organize this event. The AKC will provide information and test kits for all interested parties. Contact the AKC for details.

American Kennel Club
Attn: CGC
5580 Centerview Drive
Suite 200
Raleigh, NC 27606
919-233-9780 or 212-696-8322

Herding

A variety of herding events exist. There are noncompetitive Herding Instinct Testing and competitive Herding Trials. For more information about herding, contact the following groups.

American Herding Breed Association
1548 Victoria Way
Pacific, CA 94044
216-941-6330

American Kennel Club
5580 Centerview Drive
Suite 200
Raleigh, NC 27606
919-233-9767

Agility Trials

This sport is as much fun to watch as it is to participate. It's basically an obstacle course for dogs that's judged on speed and accuracy. The obstacle course includes jumping hurdles, running through tunnels, scaling ramps, crossing a narrow raised dog walk, traversing a see-saw, and weaving through poles. The course is completed with the dog off-leash and the handler beside them. It's an exciting activity that blends training and athletic ability. Contact these groups for more information.

US Dog Agility Association
PO Box 850955
Richardson, TX 75085-0955
214-231-9700

American Kennel Club
5580 Centerview Drive
Suite 200
Raleigh, NC 27606
919-233-9767

United Kennel Club
100 East Kilgore Road
Kalamazoo, MI 49001-5598
616-343-9020

National Committee for Agility
916-966-5287

Field Trials & Hunting Clubs

Field Trials and Hunting Tests demonstrate dogs ability to perform in the field. This may include pointing, flushing birds, retrieving, tracking, or style. Contact these groups for more information.

American Kennel Club
5580 Centerview Drive
Suite 200
Raleigh, NC 27606
919-233-9767

United Kennel Club
100 East Kilgore Road
Kalamazoo, MI 49001-5598
616-343-9020

Tracking Tests

Tracking Tests demonstrate a dog's ability to follow a scent trail. For more information, please contact these clubs.

American Kennel Club
5580 Centerview Drive
Suite 200
Raleigh, NC 27606
919-233-9767

United Kennel Club
100 East Kilgore Road
Kalamazoo, MI 49001-5598
616-343-9020

Flyball

Flyball is team sport made up of four dogs per team. It is a competitive relay race. Each dog is required to jump four hurdles and retrieve a tennis ball by stepping on a spring-loaded box that shoots out the ball. The dog catches the ball and returns to the start line. The next team member then starts until all team members have finished. Two teams compete against each other. The first team to finish without errors wins. To find out more about Flyball, contact the following groups.

North American Flyball Association
PO Box 8
Mount Hope, ON, LOR 10
Canada

Frisbee

Alpo dog food, part of the Friskies PetCare Company, sponsors the Canine Frisbee Disc Championships in communities throughout the U.S. Everyone is welcome to compete. There are no entry fees and discs are provided.

Championships include Mini-Distance and Freeflight. Mini-Distance is a timed event that is scored on a catch scale. Points are awarded on the distance of the catch along with extra points for mid-air catches. Freeflight is a timed event that is scored on degree of difficulty, execution, leaping agility, and showmanship.

Contact Friskies for more information.

Friskies Canine Frisbee Disc Championship
PO Box 725
Encino, CA 91426
800-423-3268

Friskies Canine Frisbee Disc Championship
4060-D Peachtree Rd #326
Atlanta, GA 30319
800-786-9240

Lure Coursing

This activity is designed for breeds that hunt by sight. The dogs chase a lure (simulated live game) over an open course. The lure is dragged across the ground at fast speeds in an irregular pattern much like a live game. Lure Coursing tests the dogs speed, ability to follow the lure, enthusiasm, endurance, and agility. For more information, contact the following groups.

American Sighthound Field Association
Newcomer Information Services
860-560-0533

American Kennel Club
5580 Centerview Drive, Suite 200
Raleigh, NC 27606
919-233-9767

Schutzhund

This German sport tests a dogs endurance, ability to scent, courage, mental stability, and trainability. It combines tracking, obedience, and protection exercises. Contact the USCA for more information.

USCA - United Schutzhund Club of America
3704 Lemoy Ferry Road
St. Louis, MO 63125
314-638-9686

Coonhound

Only Coonhounds participate in this sport. The dogs track and tree raccoons. Once the raccoons are treed, the dog signals the handler. To learn more about this sport, contact the following clubs.

American Kennel Club
5580 Centerview Drive
Suite 200
Raleigh, NC 27606

919-233-9767
United Kennel Club
100 East Kilgore Road
Kalamazoo, MI 49001-5598
616-343-9020

Cat Clubs

There are a number of cat registries that sponsor cat shows and clubs throughout the U.S.

American Cat Fanciers' Association
PO Box 203
Point Lookout, MO 65726
417-334-5430

Cat Fanciers' Association
1805 Atlantic Avenue
Manasquan, NJ 08736
908-528-9797

International Cat Association
PO Box 2684
Harlingen, TX 78551
210-428-8046

American Cat Association
8101 Katherine Ave
Panorama City, CA 91402
818-781-5656

Pet Pages

6 Volunteer Opportunities

Non-profit groups are always in need of volunteers or donations. Volunteering can mean hands-on activities like walking dogs, playing with cats, picking up after them, petting them, and grooming. Other activities may include adoption counseling, event participation, education programs, and administrative help. The volunteer "needs" list goes on and on. Volunteer organizations can always use financial

Pet Pages

donations and most groups usually have a wish-list of needed items like leashes, chew toys, cat toys, etc.

Many groups allow children to participate. However, there may be a minimum age requirement. In addition, some groups have a minimum time commitment. For example, they may ask volunteers to commit to a six-month volunteer obligation.

If you are interested in donating your time or money, below is a list of groups that would love your participation. Call and ask what programs are available. You're bound to find a group that fits your interests. Your help is genuinely appreciated no matter how big or small!

San Diego County Non-Profit Groups Seeking Volunteers

North County Humane Society & SPCA   (619) 757-4357
2905 San Luis Rey Road, Oceanside

Escondido Humane Society   (619) 745-4362
Picks up stray animals. Educates children and public on animal care for the City of Escondido.
3000 Las Palmas Avenue, Escondido

Helen Woodward Animal Center   (619) 756-3791
Support a place where people help animals and animals help people. Volunteers assist Center activities in a variety of departments. Meetings held the first Saturday of the month, 9 a.m. to noon.
6525 Calle del Nido, Rancho Santa Fe.

Rancho Coastal Humane Society   (619) 753-6413
A private non-profit animal shelter and adoption center in Encinitas.
389 Requeza Street, Encinitas

Volunteer Opportunities 75

San Diego Humane Society (619) 299-7012
Investigates animal abuse, educates public
on proper care of animals, adoption of pets to
new homes.
887 Sherman Street, San Diego

Friends of Cats (619) 561-0361
15587 Olde Highway 80, El Cajon

National Cat Protection Society (NCPS) (619) 469-8771
NCPS was founded to provide a safe haven
for cats without homes. Their purpose is to
educate the public about humane treatment
of cats, to provide shelter for homeless cats
until they're adopted, and to maintain a
Retirement Center for cats.
9031 Birch Street, Spring Valley

Greyhound Pets of America (619) 443-0940
A volunteer organization that rescues,
rehabilitates, and places retired racing
greyhounds in quality homes.
PO Box 2433, La Mesa, CA 91943

FOCAS (619) 685-3536
Friends of County Animal Shelters is
dedicated to a strong adoption program for
the many lost and abandoned animals at the
three public shelters, operated by the San
Diego County Department of Animal Control.
PO Box 8375, La Jolla, CA 92038

Canine Companions for Independence (619) 754-3300
CCI raises and trains dogs to help disabled
persons other than the blind, lead fuller, more
independent lives.
PO Box 4568, Oceanside, CA 92052

Feral Cat Coalition (619) 497-1599
Spays and neuters wild cats

SNAP (619) 525-3047
Spay Neuter Action Project

Central County Animal Shelter (619) 595-4558
5480 Gaines Street, San Diego

Pet Pages

South County Animal Shelter   (619) 595-4558
5821 Sweetwater Road, Bonita

North County Animal Shelter   (619) 595-4558
2481 Palomar Airport Road, Carlsbad

Coronado Animal Shelter   (619) 522-7371
578 Orange Avenue, Coronado

Chula Vista Animal Shelter   (619) 691-5123
690 Otay Valley Road, Chula Vista

El Cajon Animal Shelter   (619) 441-1580
1275 North Marshall Avenue, El Cajon

7 Travel

Just because your little Fifi has been hinting for a vacation doesn't necessarily mean she's well-suited for travel. In fact, most pets are creatures of habit and probably prefer the familiar surroundings of home to the exciting world of travel. For some pets, changing routines can be very upsetting, while other pets relish the chance to spend quality time with you exploring new places. Before taking your pet on a trip, consider the overall well-being of your pet. Does your pet enjoy rides in the car, how will she do with extended drive time? Will she be a participant in the vacation or will she be left behind bored, worried, or frightened in the hotel?

Before taking your pet, talk with your veterinarian to ensure your pet is ready for the rigors of travel. Age, temperament, and health are all factors to be considered.

Be sure your pet is welcome. Don't assume an invitation for your family includes your pet. Even though you consider your pet part of the family, your hosts may not. Confirm accommodations for your pet.

Don't Take a Pet on a Trip if It is . . .

- very shy
- aggressive
- unmanageable
- sick
- prone to motion sickness
- a female and in heat
- not housebroken
- not obedience trained
- not good with strangers

Packing For Your Pet

Taking a pet on a trip requires some preparation. Here's a list of recommended items to include in your packing.

- pet bed
- favorite pet toys or chews
- pet ID tags and license

Travel

- room deodorizer (good for car and overnight stays)
- collar and leash
- any current medication(s)
- towels
- cleaning supplies (accidents can happen anywhere)
- paper towels
- pet treats
- pet food
- pet first-aid kit (2" bandages, antibiotic ointments, gauze, tape, hydrogen peroxide, alcohol, tweezers)
- food and water bowls
- plenty of water
- (Dog) scoop
- (Cat) Litter box and litter
- health certificate
- pre-moistened towelettes
- recent photo
- crate (if pet has been trained)

Airplane Travel

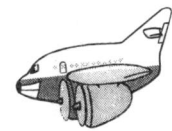

Unless you absolutely must transport your pet by air, avoid taking pets on airplanes. Carefully consider the necessity of the trip. Is this the only way to get your pet to your destination? Must he go on this trip? Pet parents are risking their pet's health, safety and even life when putting him on an airplane. Are these risks absolutely worth taking?

Pets That Should Not Fly

- Pug-nosed cats or dogs (Chow Chows, Persians, Pekinese, etc.). Because of their short nasal passages, these pets are vulnerable to oxygen deprivation and heat stroke while in the cargo area.
- Pets less than 8 weeks old
- Females in heat
- Sick or frail pets
- Pregnant pets

Talk to your veterinarian about your plans to travel. Does your veterinarian believe that your pet is in good health to travel? Should your pet have any medication to help reduce the stress? Or, would medication do more harm than good? Airlines will require a health certificate and documentation of rabies shots and vaccinations before flight.

Make your reservations with the airline early. There is a limit to the number of pets that can travel on each flight. Avoid traveling during busy times of the year such as holidays or spring break. Book direct flights to reduce stress on your pet and to avoid baggage handlers losing your pet during a connection. Your luggage won't mind a night in Beijing, but your St. Bernard would. Each minute in the airport is bound to be stressful for your pet. If the airline tries to re-route you or book you on a later flight ask questions and express your concerns. Knowing that you're traveling with a pet will enable the airlines to more precisely accommodate your needs.

Consider climate when booking your flight. Cargo areas are not temperature controlled. Book evening flights in hot weather and day time flights in cold weather. For the safety of your pet, do not fly when it is either less than 40 degrees or more than 80 degrees in either the city you are departing from and arriving in.

Before boarding the plane, ask the flight attendant to remind the captain that your pet is aboard. Confirm that he has boarded. And by all means, report mishandling of any pets by airline employees.

Airline Approved Pet Carriers

Airlines will require that your pet travel in an approved crate or pet carrier. Attach a "Live Pet" tag that contains your name, address, telephone number, and flight information. Some people include a note such as:

> *Hi, my name is Felix and I'm very nervous. This is my first flight and I'm having high anxiety. Please be gentle with me.*

This is a nice reminder to airline personnel to take extra care of your beloved pet.

Be sure the latch is secured, but not locked. In the case of an emergency, airline personnel may need to release pets. If your pet carrier fits under your seat, your pet can travel in the main cabin with you.

Layer the bottom of the carrier with newspaper to insulate and absorb moisture. For your pet's peace of mind add a towel, blanket, or an old piece of your clothing to remind him of you. Food and water bowls should be secured in a crate or attached to the outside of the crate. Do not leave food in the crate. Fill water bowl with a block of ice to avoid water spilling.

Before Departure

- Clip your pet's nails to ensure they do not hook onto the crate door or other objects.
- Pack a current photo of your pet in case he is lost in transit.
- Thoroughly exercise your pet before the flight.
- Do not feed your pet 12 hours prior to flight (water is fine until leaving).
- Before boarding, take your pet for a walk and encourage him to go to the bathroom.

Upon Arrival

You've made it! Immediately take your pet out of carrier and examine him for injury and distress. Take him to a veterinarian immediately if there are any problems. If all seems well, congratulate your travel hound, give him some water, and take him for a walk.

Car Travel

When taking pets on car trips, preparation can minimize stress and maximize comfort for your pet and you. Before you begin your trip, make sure your pet has identification tags on. Bring along his collar, leash, first aid kit, water and bowl, and waste bags. Remember his current health records and recent photos, too. Encourage him to go to the bathroom before you leave. Plan on stopping every two-to-four hours for water, exercise, and bathroom breaks.

The best place to keep your pet is in the back seat and preferably in a crate. Cats are more comfortable and safer in their carriers. There are also seatbelt harnesses available for dogs.

Be sensitive to the fact that the temperature in the

back seat may be different than what you are experiencing in the front. Just because you're doing fine doesn't mean your pet is too.

While you want to get lots of fresh air circulating around the car, be cautious when allowing dogs to stick their heads out the window. He'll get a cool breeze, but he may also get hit by debris. An airborne pebble can be mighty painful if it hits your pet in the eyes, nose, mouth, or face. Cold air may also harm pets lungs, so do not let him keep his head out the window for extended periods. For these reasons and other safety risks, do not use open flatbed trucks to transport pets.

Be sure pets have plenty of room to move around comfortably. Include your pet on rest stops so he gets a chance to get out of the car and move about. Leaving your pet alone in the car invites pet theft and can be dangerous on warm days. During these breaks, be sure to keep your pet on a leash.

Pack food in heavy-duty zip lock bags. Heavy duty plastic bags also work well for water bowls. Keep a water bowl with water or ice available to pet. When you park, find a shady spot so pets don't overheat in the car.

To avoid sickness, allow one hour for pets to digest food. Be sensitive to signs of motion sickness. Drooling, restlessness, anxiety, vomiting, and looking distressed are all signs of potential trouble.

Even on cool days, the sun can heat up a car quickly. But on hot days, the risk of overheating your pet is even greater. The temperature inside a car can reach deadly temperatures in a matter of minutes, and that's with the windows partially opened! Overheating can cause brain damage and death; never leave your pet in a car on a warm day, even with the windows cracked. Don't do it.

Pet Pages

On cooler days, when you must leave your pet in the car, be sure to park in the shade. Leave the windows cracked, but not enough to allow someone to break in or to allow your pet to get caught. Set a bowl of cool water on the floor.

Check the EMERGENCY CARE section for treating heat stroke.

Hotel Stays

If your travels require an overnight stay, there are thousands of hotels in the United States that welcome pets. Hotels expect your pet to be house-trained and well-behaved. Basic courtesies will go a long way in keeping pets welcome at these hotels.

Be Kind to Pet-Friendly Hotels By . . .

- picking up after your pet
- acknowledging and paying for any damages
- feeding your pet on the bathroom floor.
- setting pet's towel or blanket down on his sleeping area to prevent shedding on furniture, bed, or carpet
- confirming your pet's reservation along with yours

Be Kind to Your Pet By . . .

- bringing his favorite toys, blanket, or bed
- keeping him on a leash to minimize his chances of getting lost
- asking hotel about exercise areas for pets
- taking him with you, not leaving him in the hotel

Travel

- leaving information about where you are and when you'll be back at the front desk (if you absolutely must leave pet alone).
- leaving the front desk with a telephone number and emergency instructions.
- crating him if you must leave him alone.
- leaving television on to mask noises that may frighten your pet or cause him to bark.
- See the LODGING Section for a complete listing of local accommodations that are pet-friendly.

If Pet is Lost During Travel

So, young Fifi ventured out to do some sightseeing on her own. Problem is, now she can't find her way back to you. Organize a search party immediately. Time is critical so don't delay. If you haven't found her within a few hours, call every animal shelter and humane society within 60 miles and check with them daily. Post "Lost Dog" signs with photo or description of the pet at busy intersections, stores, and veterinary clinics. Enlist the help of local letter carriers and police officers. While they walk their route and beat, they can keep an eye opened for your pet. Place a "Lost Dog" ad in the local newspaper that includes your pet's description and how to contact you. A frightened and disoriented pet can take days or weeks to allow a stranger to approach him, so be persistent. It may take a while, but keep calling and searching.

See LOST & FOUND section for more information on what to do.

What to Do if You Can't Take Your Pet

There are a number of options to consider if you must leave your pet behind. You may be fortunate enough to have a reliable friend, family member, or neighbor who gladly cares for your pet while you're away. If not, then your options are to hire a pet-sitter or to drop your pet off at a boarding kennel.

Pet-Sitters

Your friends and family will appreciate this. Given the right sitter you can travel worry-free, knowing that your home and pet are being cared for.

Not only will a pet-sitter feed, water, exercise, medicate, and play with pets, but she will also take care of your home. This may include things like watering plants, bringing in mail, opening and closing drapes, and turning lights on and off.

If your pet won't be traveling with you, it would probably be happier staying at home rather than at a kennel. Pet-sitters can either stop by a certain number of times per day or stay in your home for round-the-clock petcare. Pet-sitters can be a particularly attractive option if your pet is older or ill. Pets can become depressed or anxious while the family is away. Daily visits from a sitter will comfort your pet. Just listen to what Gus Greyhound had to say about his recent pet-sitter:

"Okay, so my parents are all like packing suitcases and humming Don Ho tunes so I know what this means — vacation time. Last time the furless ones went away, I went to a kennel. The staff was nice and all, but this cat kept sneezing and one of the puppies kept howling all night long. There was this totally cute whippet, but I hardly got a chance to bark with her. Anyway, I'm thinking, okay back to the kennel with me, but then my family just kisses me goodbye and leaves. Whoa! So I'm thinking right-on — party time! I give my super high-pitched howl so the whole neighborhood knows it's time to PARTY. But just as I'm breaking out the kibbles, I hear these keys opening the front door. It's that furless lady that was here with Mom yesterday, petting me and telling me what fun we were going to have. But I don't want her at my party. All the dogs will think I'm a total geek having a human chaperon. But wait, she brought in the mail and the newspaper and watered the plants. Cool! That's one less thing for me to do. Then she closed the drapes, filled my food bowl, and cleaned out the cat litter. (I can't believe they go in the house — gross!) After that, she gave me my medication — oops, I would have forgotten about that. She then took me for a nice long walk, played ball with me in the backyard, and petted me under the chin. Before she left, she then turned on some music. Could this be? Might it be? Could this be my very own party planner? Oh yes! How cool! I'm totally psyched for the raddest party ever. Yippee, I love my parents. This beats the kennel any day of the week."

P.S. "She even played hide and seek with our cat!"

Gus was a little disappointed to discover that his sitter wasn't there to cater a party, but he soon discovered she could be useful in other ways. She kept the food coming, walked him regularly, and did little chores around the house. Overall, she kept him on his routine, and Gus was glad to have her around.

You can hire a professional pet-sitter or employ someone you already know to watch your pets while you're away. This will reduce the stress on your friends, not to mention any of your own worrying! Interview potential sitters to see how well she interacts with your pet. Does your pet seem to like the prospective sitter? Does the sitter seem affectionate, capable, and responsible?

Questions to Ask

- How long have they been in business?
- Are they licensed and bonded?
- What is their level of experience?
- How would they handle an emergency? Do they have a backup plan in case they have an emergency?
- Can they provide three references?

Things to Discuss

- Be sure sitter has specific instructions about feeding, medication, exercise, play, etc.
- Make sure they have a list of emergency telephone numbers, including your veterinarian, a neighbor, friend and a back-up sitter in case something happens to her.
- Leave your itinerary and telephone numbers.

Boarding

Before you make your reservation to board your pet, tour the facilities to be sure it is a safe and caring environment. Does the facility look and smell clean? Do the cages and runs seem big enough to comfortably suit your pet's needs? Do the other pets seem happy and well cared for? Is there adequate protection from the elements? Is the facility well-lit?

Questions to Ask

- Do they belong to the American Boarding Kennel Association?
- How many staff members are on site? What about during "closed' hours?

- How is the temperature controlled? (Do they have air-conditioning and heating?)
- How frequently are pet areas cleaned?
- How often are pets exercised or played with?
- Is there a shaded outdoor exercise area?
- How often are pets groomed?
- Are pets groomed on-site or do they take them to another facility? (When pets are transported, there is a greater risk for problems — like escapes or injuries during transport.)
- Do they allow personal items such as toys, blankets, and beds?
- Can your pet be fed her regular food to avoid diarrhea?
- What types of safety precautions are there? Are there smoke detectors, sprinklers, fire alarms, and staff on site for security?

Aside from the kennel's policies and procedures, you'll want to become acquainted with the staff and their philosophy on pet care. A loving environment will lessen the trauma of being away from home. Staff at a good kennel will handle your pet with care and sensitivity. They'll be working at the facility because they love animals and want to help make your pet's stay happy and healthy, not because there were no jobs at Wonder Burger.

If you are able, take your pet to the kennel to introduce her to the staff and show her where she will be staying. If the staff seems excited about meeting your pet and shows genuine concern for her, the kennel will probably be a good experience for your pet. If the staff rolls their eyes and mutters that you should get a life, it's probably not the environment you want for your pet.

When you drop off your pet, take some personal items to remind her of home. Her bed, blanket, or toys will help give her a sense of security. An old tee-shirt or something that smells like you will also comfort her during her stay. Remember to bring her food and medications along with any special instructions for care. It's always a good idea to leave your itinerary and emergency telephone numbers in case the kennel staff needs to reach you. Be sure to call the kennel to see how your pet is doing.

After you pick your pet up from her stay at the kennel, observe her for unusual behavior. Does she seem more aggressive? Timid? Fearful? If abnormal behavior persists, check with your veterinarian.

The downside to boarding pets at a kennel is that they are at greater risk of contracting infectious disease. Additionally, confined quarters and new environments can cause anxiety and depression.

8 Lodging

There are over a hundred hotels and motels in San Diego County that are pet-friendly. When making your reservations, be sure to confirm that you will be bringing your pet. For more tips on overnight stays, check the TRAVEL section.

You may be asking yourself, "If I live in San Diego and have a home, why do I care what hotels and motels are pet friendly?"

Well the answer is simple:

- Many pet owners treating their home for pests will, many times, stay overnight in a nearby hotel with their pets.
- Friends and family who visit may need accommodations that are pet-friendly.

The following is a list of pet-friendly accommodations in the San Diego area. Be sure to confirm that your pet meets any weight restrictions. Many of the hotels and motels only allow pets weighing less than 25 pounds. Also, ask about any additional pet fees or deposits, some of which may not be refundable. Room rates are subject to change.

Lodging

Carlsbad

INNS OF AMERICA
751 Raintree Dr. (92209)
Room Rates: $43-$57
800-826-0778

MOTEL 6
1006 Carlsbad Village Dr.
(92009)
Room Rates: $35-$48
434-7135

MOTEL 6
750 Raintree Dr. (92009)
Room Rates: $32-$51
431-0745

MOTEL 6
6117 Paseo del Norte (92009)
Room Rates: $32-$44
438-1242

Chula Vista

LA QUINTA INN
150 Bonita Rd. (91910)
Room Rates: $49-$58
691-1211

MOTEL 6
745 E St. (91910)
Room Rates: $33-$37
800-325-2525

TRAVELER MOTEL KITCHEN SUITES
235 Woodlawn Ave. (91910)
Room Rates: $43-$59
$30 pet fee
800-748-6998

TRAVELODGE
394 Broadway (91910)
Room Rates: $43-$69
619-420-6600

VAGABOND INN
230 Broadway (91910)
Room Rates: $42-$60
$10 pet fee
800-522-1555

Coronado

EL CORDOVA MOTEL
1351 Orange Ave. (92118)
Room Rates: $70-$148
800-229-2032

LOEWS CORONADO BAY RESORT
4000 Coronado Bay Road
(92118)
Room Rates: $180-$475
800-815-6397

Del Mar

DEL MAR HILTON NORTH SAN DIEGO
15575 Jimmy Durante Blvd.
(92014).
Room Rates: $85-$140
800-445-8667

El Cajon

BEST WESTERN COURTESY INN
1355 E. Main (92021)
Room Rates: $38-$57
619-440-7378

DAYS INN
1250 El Cajon Boulevard (92920)
Room Rates: $40-$60
$6 pet fee
800-325-2525

MOTEL 6
550 Montrose Ct. (92020)
Room Rates: $30-$46
588-6100

VILLA EMBASADORA
1556 E. Main St. (92021) Room Rates: $30-$45
$5 pet fee
442-9617

Encinitas

BUDGET MOTEL OF ENCINITAS
133 Encinitas Blvd. (92024)
Room Rates: $34-$62
800-795-6044

ECONO LODGE
410 N. Hwy 101 (92024)
Room Rates: $45-$65
800-221-2222

Escondido

BEST WESTERN ESCONDIDO
1700 Seven Oaks Rd. (92026)
Room Rates: $66-$78
619-740-1700

LAWRENCE WELK RESORT
8860 Lawrence Welk Dr. (92026)
Room Rates: $90-$220
800-932-9355

MOTEL 6
900 N. Quince St. (92025)
Room Rates: $35-$48
745-9252

SIX INNS
509 West Washington Ave. (92025)
Room Rates: $26-35
743-6669

SUPER 8 MOTEL
528 W. Washington Ave (92025)
Room Rates: $35-$55
Pet Deposit Required
619-747-3711

THE SHERIDAN INN
1341 N. Escondido Blvd. (92026)
Room Rates: $51-$57
800-258-8527

Fallbrook

BEST WESTERN FRANCISCAN INN
1635 S. Mission Rd. (92028)
Room Rates: $45-$65
800-528-1234

LA ESTANCIA INN
3135 S. Old Hwy 395 (92028)
Room Rates: $48-$78
$25 pet fee
723-2888

Imperial Beach

HAWAIIAN GARDENS SUITE-HOTEL
1031 Imperial Beach Blvd. (91932)
Room Rates: $60-$125
800-334-3071

Lodging

Julian

EAGLE NEST BED & BREAKFAST
2609 D St. (92036)
Room Rates: $75-$120
765-1252

LEELIN'S WIKIUP BED & BREAKFAST
1645 Whispering Pines Dr.
(92036)
Room Rates: $95-$115
765-1890

PINE HILLS LODGE
2960 La Posada, Box 2260
(92036)
Room Rates: $60-$125
765-1100

SEA STAR GUEST COTTAGE
4041 Deer Lake Park Rd.
(92036)
Room Rates: $95
765-0502

La Jolla

LA JOLLA HOLIDAY INN
6705 La Jolla Blvd. (92037)
Room Rates: $99-$189
454-7101

MARRIOTT HOTEL - LA JOLLA
4240 La Jolla Village Dr.
(92037)
Room Rates: $115-$135
800-228-9290

RESIDENCE INN BY MARRIOTT
8901 Gilman Dr. (92037)
Room Rates: $85-$140
800-331-3131

SCRIPPS INN
555 Coast Boulevard South
(92037)
Room Rates: $90-$170
454-3391

La Mesa

COMFORT INN-LA MESA
8000 Parkway Dr. (91942)
Room Rates: $39-$99
800-221-2222

MOTEL 6
7621 Alvarado Rd. (91941)
Room Rates: $32-$43
464-7151

National City

HOLIDAY INN - SOUTH BAY
700 National City Blvd. (91950)
Room Rates: $55
800-465-4329

RADISSON SUITES
810 National City Blvd. (91950)
Room Rates: $69-$79
$20 pet deposit
800-333-3333

Oceanside

MOTEL 6-EAST
3708 Plaza Dr. (92056)
Room Rates: $36-$45
941-1011

MOTEL 6-NORTH
1403 Mission Ave. (92054)
Room Rates: $35-$48
434-7135

SANDMAN HOTEL
1501 Carmelo Dr. (92054)
Room Rates: $36-$49
722-7661

Poway

POWAY COUNTRY INN
13845 Poway Rd. (92064)
Room Rates: $42-$75
800-648-6320

Ramona

RAMONA VALLEY INN
416 Main St. (92065)
Room Rates: $45-$50
$50 pet deposit
800-648-4618

Rancho Bernardo

CARMEL HIGHLAND
DOUBLETREE GOLF RESORT
14455 Peñasquitos Dr.
(92129)
Room Rates: $100-$179
800-622-9223

LA QUINTA MOTOR INN
10185 Paseo Montril (92129)
Room Rates: $49-$59
800-531-5900

RADISSON SUITE HOTEL
11520 W Bernardo Ct.
(92127)
Room Rates: $79-$119
619-451-6600

RANCHO BERNARDO INN
17550 Bernardo Oaks (92128)
Room Rates: $195-$265
$50 pet fee
800-542-6096

RESIDENCE INN BY MARRIOTT
11002 Rancho Carmel Dr.
(92128)
Room Rates: $79-$149
$150 pet deposit
800-331-3131

TRAVELODGE
16929 W Bernardo Dr. (92127)
Room Rates: $50-$62
$5 pet fee/$25 pet deposit
800-578-7878

Rancho Santa Fe

INN AT RANCHO SANTA FE
5951 Linea del Cielo (92067)
Room Rates: $95-$195
756-1131

San Diego

BEACH HAVEN INN
4740 Mission Blvd. (92109)
Room Rates: $60-$140
800-831-6323

BEST WESTERN - SEVEN SEAS
411 Hotel Circle S. (92108)
Room Rates: $50-$99
800-528-1234

Lodging

CROWN POINT VIEW SUITE-HOTEL
4088 Crown Point Dr. (92109)
Room Rates: $70-$150
$50 pet fee
800-338-3331

FOUR POINTS BY SHERATON HOTEL
8110 Aero Dr. (92123)
Room Rates: $85-$93
$100 pet deposit
800-421-6662

GOOD NITE INN
4545 Waring Rd. (92101)
Room Rates: $35-$55
286-7000

GROSVENOR INN
810 Ash St. (92101)
Room Rates: $50-$70
$20 pet fee
800-232-1212

HANALEI HOTEL
2270 Hotel Circle N. (92108)
Room Rates: $69-$119
$50 pet fee
800-882-0858

HOLIDAY INN ON THE BAY
1355 North Harbor Dr. (92101)
Room Rates: $70-$100
800-877-8920

LAMPLIGHTER INN
6474 El Cajon Blvd. (92115)
Room Rates: $43-$97
$5 pet fee
800-545-0778

MARRIOTT SAN DIEGO MARINA
333 West Harbor Dr. (92101)
Room Rates: $150-$180
800-228-9290

MARRIOTT SUITES - DOWNTOWN
701 A St. (92101)
Room Rates: $149-$179
$50 pet fee
800-962-1367

MOTEL 6 - HOTEL CIRCLE
2424 Hotel Circle N. (92108)
Room Rates: $36-$42
296-1612

MOTEL 6 - NORTH
5592 Clairemont Mesa Blvd. (92117)
Room Rates: $34-$40
268-9758

PACIFIC SHORES INN
4802 Mission Blvd. (92109)
Room Rates: $58-$95
$25 pet fee
800-826-0715

PARK MANOR SUITES
525 Spruce St. (92103)
Room Rates: $79-$139
$30 pet fee
800-874-2649

RAMADA INN - SAN DIEGO NORTH
5550 Kearny Mesa Rd. (92111)
Room Rates: $52-$84
800-447-2637

RED LION INN
7450 Hazard Center Dr. (92108)
Room Rates: $124-$150
800-547-8010

RESIDENCE INN
5400 Kearny Mesa Rd. (92111)
Room Rates: $69-$175
800-331-3131

SAN DIEGO HILTON BEACH & TENNIS
1775 E. Mission Bay Dr. (92109)
Room Rates: $145-$225
800-962-6307

SAN DIEGO MARRIOTT MISSION VALLEY
8757 Rio San Diego Dr. (92108)
Room Rates: $109-$139
$200 pet deposit
692-3800

SAN DIEGO MISSION VALLEY HILTON
901 Camino Del Rio S. (92108)
Room Rates: $89-$149
800-733-2332

SAN DIEGO PRINCESS RESORT
1404 West Vacation Road (92109)
Room Rates: $115-$240
800-344-2626

SOUTH BAY LODGE
1101 Hollister St. (92154)
Room Rates: $27-$47
429-7600

SUPER 8 MISSION BAY
4540 Mission Bay Dr. (92109)
Room Rates: $45-$58
800-800-8000

THE VAGABOND INN - MISSION VALLEY
625 Hotel Circle South (92108)
Room Rates: $42-$65
$10 pet fee
800-522-1555

THE VAGABOND INN — POINT LOMA
1325 Scott St. (92106)
Room Rates: $42-$70
800-522-1555

THE VAGABOND INN - UNIVERSITY
6440 El Cajon Blvd. (92115)
Room Rates: $40-$55
800-522-1555

US GRANT HOTEL
Broadway (92101)
Room Rates: $135- $195
(Ask about the Pampered Pet Program)
800-237-5029

San Marcos

LAKE SAN MARCOS RESORT/ QUAILS INN
1025 La Bonita Dr. (92069)
Room Rates: $85-$225
$10 pet fee
800-447-6556

Lodging

San Ysidro

ECONOMY INNS OF AMERICA
230 Via de San Ysidro (92173)
Room Rates: $25-$40
800-826-0778

INTERNATIONAL MOTOR INN
190 E. Calle Primera (92173)
Room Rates: $40-$55
619-428-4486

MOTEL 6
160 E. Calle Primera (92173)
Room Rates: $26-$30
619-690-6663

Spring Valley

SUPER 8 MOTEL
9603 Campo Rd. (91977)
Room Rates: $37-$49
800-800-8000

Vista

HILLTOP MOTOR LODGE
330 Mar Vista Dr. (92083)
Room Rates: $36-$50
$5-$10 pet fee
619-726-7010

LA QUINTA INN
630 Sycamore Ave. (92083)
Room Rates: $46-$61
800-221-4731

Pet Pages

9 Emergency Care

This section deals with two types of emergencies. First, accidents that require immediate first-aid and secondly, natural disasters that require emergency responses. Although you are probably not in a crisis at this moment, please review this section so that you will be better prepared to face an emergency should it arise.

Accidents

Accidents happen unexpectedly and your veterinarian may not always be available at the time and place you need him. Please take the time to familiarize yourself with the following emergency first-aid procedures so you are prepared to provide immediate care. Knowledge of first-aid procedures may save the life of your pet in an emergency.

If possible, call your veterinarian or an emergency care facility to coach you over the phone. And always follow-up with professional medical care from your veterinarian. Even if your pet seems fine after you've provided immediate care, he may have internal injuries. Pets can appear to be fully recovered, then worsen days later.

If your pet is injured, do not give him water or other liquids. In case of internal injury, this could make his condition worse rather than provide the relief you intended.

Pet First Aid

In an emergency, first aid is not a substitute for veterinary treatment. However, if you are unable to get your pet to a veterinarian, knowing basic first-aid could save your pet's life. Always seek veterinary care following first-aid attempts.

Emergency Care

BITE WOUNDS — Approach the pet carefully to avoid getting bitten. Muzzle the animal. Clean the wound with large amounts of water. Wrap large open wounds to keep them clean. Apply pressure to profusely bleeding wounds. Bite wounds often become infected and need professional care. Call veterinarian.

BLEEDING — Apply firm, direct pressure over the bleeding area until the bleeding stops. Avoid bandages that cut off circulation. Call veterinarian immediately.

BREATHING (pet stops breathing) — Check to see if the animal is choking on a foreign object (See CHOKING)

If an object is removed from the throat and the animal still is not breathing, place the animal with its right side down. Close the animal's mouth and exhale directly into the nose, not mouth, until the chest expands. Cover the nose with a handkerchief or a thin cloth if preferred. Exhale 12 to 15 times per minute. At the same time apply heart massage with the other hand. The heart is located in the lower half of the chest behind the elbow of the front left leg. Place hand over the heart and compress the chest 1 to 2 inches for large animals, 1 inch for small animals. Apply heart massage 70-90 times per minute. Call veterinarian immediately.

CHOKING difficulty breathing, excessive pawing at mouth, blue lips and tongue.

Look into the mouth to see if foreign object in throat is visible. Clear the airway by removing the object with pliers or tweezers, being careful not to push it farther down the throat. If the object remains lodged, place your hands on both sides of the animal's rib cage and apply firm, quick pressure. Or place the animal on its side and strike the side of the rib cage firmly with the palm of your hand 3 or 4 times. Repeat this procedure until the object is dislodged. Call veterinarian immediately. (See BREATHING).

DIARRHEA Withhold food for 12-24 hours. Give ice cubes only. Call veterinarian.

FOREIGN OBJECTS IMBEDDED

Porcupine quills

Sharp, hollow shafts.
Quill cannot be pulled out without anesthesia. Call veterinarian.

Foxtails

A barbed seed sometimes visible in eye, nose, mouth, throat or skin causing severe irritation. Foxtails are usually too deep to remove without general anesthetic. Call veterinarian.

Emergency Care

BURNS (Chemical, electrical and heat)

singed hair, blistering, swelling, redness of skin

Flush burn area immediately with large amounts of cold water. Apply ice pack for 15-20 minutes. Call veterinarian immediately.

FRACTURES

pain, inability to use leg

Muzzle animal and control bleeding. Watch for any sigh of shock. DO NOT TRY TO RESET A FRACTURE. Transport the animal to the veterinarian immediately using a stretcher. Call veterinarian immediately.

HEAT STROKE

rapid or difficulty breathing, vomiting, high body temperature, collapse

Place animal in a tub of cold water, gently soak with a garden hose or wrap in a cold, wet towel. Call veterinarian immediately.

INSECT BITES

onset of swelling, itching and pain within one hour of bite.

Remove stinger and apply cold packs. If isolated from veterinary care, a topical cortisone or an anti-inflammatory ointment can be rubbed on area of bite. A previously prescribed antihistamine may be give orally. Call veterinarian.

SEIZURES

salivation, loss of control of urine or stool, violent muscle twitching, loss of consciousness.

Move pet away from any objects that could be harmful. Use a blanket for padding and protection. Do not put yourself at risk by restraining the animal during the seizure. Time the seizure: it usually lasts only 2 or 3 minutes. Afterwards, keep the animal calm, quiet and cool. Call veterinarian immediately.

POISONING

vomiting, convulsions, diarrhea, salivation, weakness, depression, pain

Write down what the ingested and how much. Immediately call the veterinarian or poison control center. Do not induce vomiting or attempt treatment without direction from the doctor.

In the case of poisoning on the fur/skin from oils, paints or chemicals, wash the animal with mild soap and rinse well. Call veterinarian.

Poison Control:

Poison Control Hotline	619-543-6000
Emergency Number $30 Charge	800-548-2423
Non-Emergency	900-680-0000

$20 for first 5 min, $2.95 additional min ($30 maximum charge)

Major credit cards accepted.

SHOCK

irregular breathing, dilated pupils

May occur with serious injury or fright. Keep animal gently restrained, quiet and warm with head elevated. Call veterinarian immediately.

SNAKEBITE (poisonous & nonpoisonous)

rapid swelling, skin puncture, pain, weakness, shock

Stop all exercise to prevent spread of venom. Clean area. Many poisons damage nerves or body tissue on contact. Call veterinarian immediately.

VOMITING

Withhold food for 12-24 hours. Give ice cubes for two hours after vomiting stops. Then slowly increase the amount of water and foods given over a 24-hour period. Call veterinarian.

EQUIPMENT:

Muzzle
Use a strip of soft cloth, rope, necktie or nylon stocking. Wrap around the nose, under the chin and tie behind the ears. Care must be taken when handling weak or injured animals. Even normally docile pets will bite when in pain. Allow animal to pant after handling by loosing or removing the muzzle. Do not use a muzzle in a case of vomiting. Cats and small pets may be difficult to muzzle. A towel placed around the head will help control small pets.

Stretcher
A door, board, blanket or floor mat can be used as a stretcher to transport injured or weak animals.

Natural Disasters

Since you cannot prevent natural disasters, the next best thing to do is prepare for them. When your family has emergency supplies and plans for a flood, hurricane, fire, earthquake, and tornado, it can minimize the impact of these disasters.

Emergency Supplies

Keep supplies together in a sealed waterproof container that will be easily accessible in an emergency. An old duffel bag or backpack will fare well against the elements.

- ✓ activated charcoal tablets
- ✓ can-opener if needed for food or supplies
- ✓ carriers/crates for pets
- ✓ collar and leash
- ✓ copies of health certificate, license, and vaccination
- ✓ cotton balls and swabs
- ✓ diarrhea medicine
- ✓ emergency phone numbers (veterinarian, pet care)
- ✓ flame retardant blankets
- ✓ flea products
- ✓ food and water bowls
- ✓ food and water (two-week supply)
- ✓ litter and pan
- ✓ medication (two-week supply)
- ✓ pet first-aid kit (2" bandages, antibiotic ointments, gauze, tape, hydrogen peroxide, alcohol, tweezers)
- ✓ petroleum jelly

Emergency Care

- ✓ plastic bags for waste
- ✓ recent photos
- ✓ rectal thermometer
- ✓ scissors

Emergency Drills

Decide in advance who does what in an emergency. Which family member will gather pets and supplies? Have regular emergency drills to keep the plan fresh in the minds of your family members. Post emergency stickers on your front door or window to notify fire fighters that pets are inside. Fire fighters will make every attempt to save your pet.

Emergency Information

EMERGENCY PET HOSPITALS

#	Name	Address	City	Phone
1	LA COSTA ANIMAL HOSPITAL	7750 El Camino Real # G	Carlsbad	944-1266
2	SOUTH COUNTY ANIMAL CLINIC	3438 Bonita Rd	Chula Vista	427-2881
3	ALL CREATURES HOSPITAL	3665 Via De La Valle	Del Mar	481-7992
4	NORTH COAST VETERINARY	285 N El Camino Real # 105	Encinitas	632-1072
5	ESCONDIDO SMALL ANIMAL HOSP	630 Enterprise St	Escondido	745-4515
6	ESCONDIDO URGENT CARE		Excondido	PET-9600
7	ANIMAL HOSPITAL OF LA JOLLA	7601 Draper Ave	La Jolla	459-2665
8	A PET EMERGENCY CLINIC	5232 Jackson Dr # 105	La Mesa	462-4800
9	PLAZA BOULEVARD PET CLINIC	2415 E Plaza Blvd	National City	267-8200
10	TEMPLE HEIGHTS PET HOSP	4750 Oceanside Blvd # A2	Oceanside	630-3590
11	ADOBE ANIMAL HOSPITAL	1134 D St	Ramona	789-7090
12	CHRISTOPHER GEORGE DVM	1357 Barnett Rd	Ramona	789-5120
13	ABC VETERINARY HOSPITALS	2032 Hornblend St	San Diego	270-4120
14	ALL CARE CAT HOSPITAL	4680 Clairemont Mesa Blvd	San Diego	274-2287
15	ANIMAL EMERGENCY CLINIC	13240 Evening Creek Dr S	San Diego	748-7387
16	COLINA VETERINARY HOSPITAL	5530 University Ave	San Diego	286-3360
17	EMERGENCY ANIMAL CLINIC	2317 Hotel Cir S	San Diego	299-2400
18	PACIFIC PETCARE VETERINARY	12720 Carmel Country Rd	San Diego	481-1101
19	PALM RIDGE PET HOSPITAL	4370 Palm Ave # S	San Diego	690-2272
20	SAN CARLOS VET. HOSPITAL	8618 Lake Murray Blvd	San Diego	460-3100
21	PALOMAR ANIMAL HOSPITAL	2615 S Santa Fe Ave	San Marcos	727-7622
22	SAN MARCOS ANIMAL CTR	325 S Rancho Santa Fe Rd # D	San Marcos	744-7410
23	MISSION GORGE VET. HOSP	9302 Carlton Hills Blvd	Santee	258-1150
24	PARADISE VALLEY PET HOSP	8360 Paradise Valley Rd # B	Spring Valley	263-0345
25	EMERGENCY ANIMAL CLINIC	1925 W Vista Way	Vista	724-7444

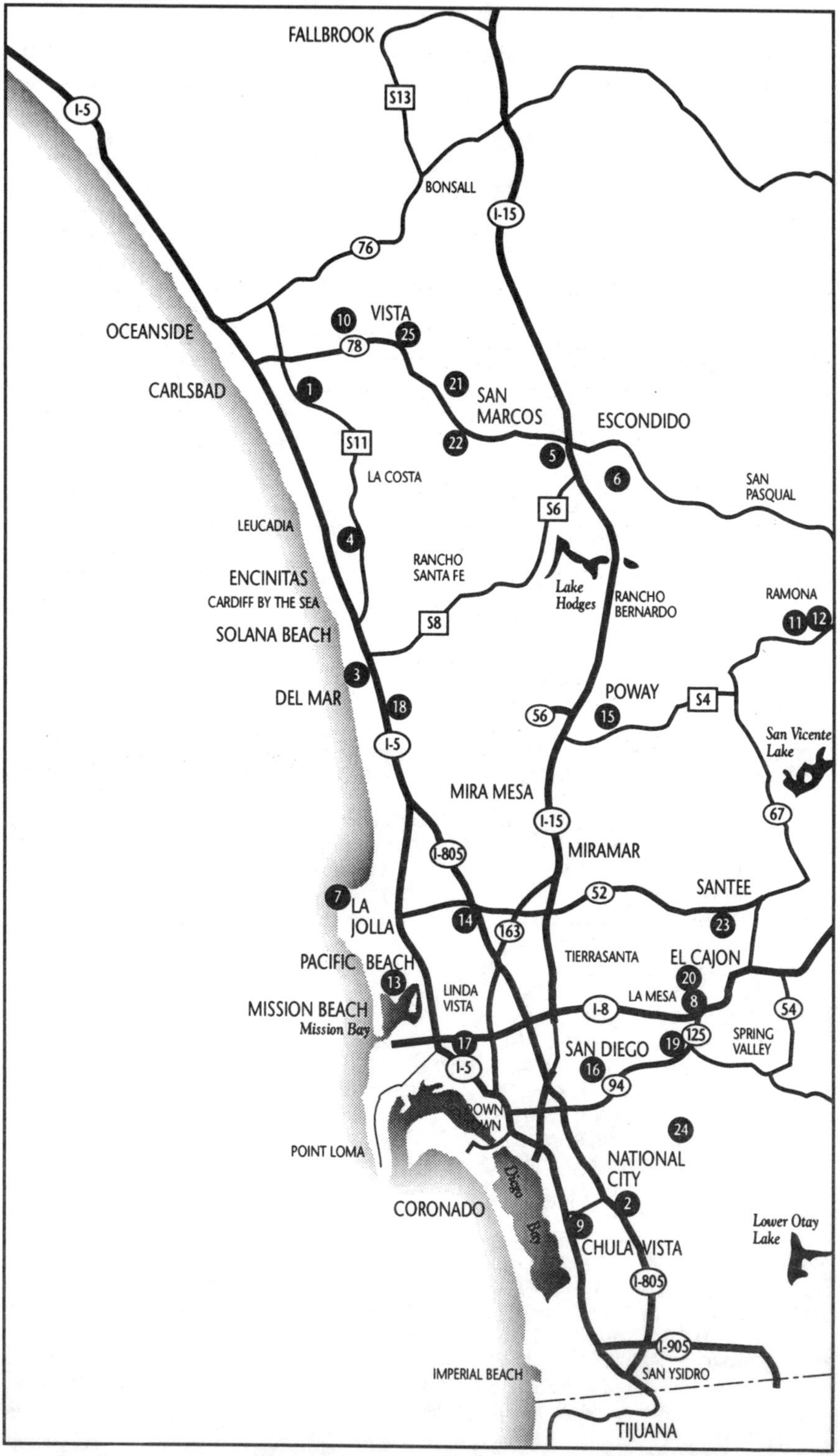
FALLBROOK
I-5
S13
BONSALL
I-15
76
10
VISTA
OCEANSIDE
78
25
CARLSBAD
1
21
SAN MARCOS
ESCONDIDO
S11
22
5
LA COSTA
6
SAN PASQUAL
S6
LEUCADIA
4
RANCHO SANTA FE
ENCINITAS
Lake Hodges
RANCHO BERNARDO
CARDIFF BY THE SEA
RAMONA
S8
11
12
SOLANA BEACH
3
DEL MAR
POWAY
18
S4
56
15
I-5
San Vicente Lake
MIRA MESA
67
I-15
MIRAMAR
I-805
7
52
SANTEE
LA JOLLA
14
163
23
TIERRASANTA
EL CAJON
PACIFIC BEACH
13
20
LINDA VISTA
LA MESA
MISSION BEACH
I-8
8
54
Mission Bay
125
SPRING VALLEY
17
19
SAN DIEGO
I-5
16
94
DOWNTOWN
24
POINT LOMA
NATIONAL CITY
Diego Bay
2
CORONADO
9
Lower Otay Lake
CHULA VISTA
I-805
I-905
IMPERIAL BEACH
SAN YSIDRO
TIJUANA

Lost & Found Pets 111

10 Lost & Found Pets

Aside from a trip to the veterinarian, nothing is more frightening for a pet than being lost. All that's familiar to your pet is suddenly gone and has been replaced with the unknown.

Simple precautions can help find a lost pet, or better yet, prevent the problem all together. Make sure all pets have identification tags that include your home telephone number. Have a clear color photo of your pet on hand to help others identify him.

Train your pet not to dart out the door, and never leave your pet unattended in a parking lot or outside of a store.

Check Inside the House

If your pet turns up missing despite these precautionary measures, the first place to search is around the house. Think about places you might have accidentally trapped your pet like the attic, basement, closet, or cabinets.

Dangerous Liaisons

Check the refrigerator right away. Your pet isn't likely to be there, but in the rare event she is, your chilly dog or cold kitty will greatly appreciate a quick escape to room temperature. If your washer and dryer are running, check them immediately.

The spin cycle is no place for a land-loving pet.

Other Places in the House

Pets are curious little critters and want to explore areas of the house. Think about all the places small enough to fit your pet. Could kitty have filed himself in your file cabinet? Could he be immersed in a great novel behind the bookshelf? Perhaps he's tucked away in your Lazy Boy? Small pets love to explore the world of box springs and bedding. Kitty may be a Santa Claus impersonator and be hiding in the fireplace. (If you find him there, remember to wash paws thoroughly to avoid a house full of cinderprints.) You may find your pet in a suitcase. (If he's wearing your Hawaiian shorts, your clever kitty is telling you he needs a vacation.) How about in or behind an appliance? If kitty shows talent for vacuuming and the like, you may want to consider cultivating these fine skills.

Your Search Outside

If you are still unable to find your pet, organize a search party immediately both by car and by foot. Call your pet by name and listen carefully. Leave his favorite person's laundry on the doorstep and walk barefoot so the pet can track the scent home. Ask neighbors, mail carriers, and garbage collectors if they have seen your pet. Copy a photograph of your pet to post with a "Lost Pet" sign. On your sign, include a photo, the pet's name and breed, and a telephone number to call for people to reach you. Offering a reward will greatly enhance your chances of recovering your pet. Distribute these fliers within a two-to-three mile radius from home, at local veterinary offices, animal shelters, pet stores, neighbors' homes, and on telephone poles.

Go to local animal shelters to see if anyone has found your pet; don't rely on anyone else to identify your pet for you. Place a lost ad in the local newspaper. Check the found ads. Many papers offer this service for free.

Finally, don't give up. It could take weeks or even months to find your lost pet. He's trying to find you just as hard as you are trying to find him. Usually, it's just a matter of time before you reconnect with your wayward pet.

Found Pets

If you find a pet, approach him calmly and cautiously. Be sensitive to the fact that the pet is already frightened and will be alarmed by sudden moves. Check for identification tags. If there are tags, then contact the owner immediately. If there are no tags, have the pet checked for a microchip ID.

If the pet is injured, call animal control for assistance or take him to your veterinarian.

The first place to call is the animal shelter to find out if anyone is looking for the pet. The owner will likely call here first as well. Contact lost and found services, check lost ads in the newspaper, and talk to your neighbors. You should also place a found ad in the local paper.

If you are able, keep the pet at your home. Meanwhile, take a photograph of the pet and post "Found Pet" notices around town. While you're out, be on the lookout for "Lost Pet" signs. If you site a station wagon full of kids sobbing, "Lassie, come home," your days of surrogate pooch parenthood are probably over. On the other hand, if someone shows up claiming to be the owner, be sure to check for proof. A photo or veterinarian bill will suffice. If the person is unable to provide this information and the pet doesn't seem to recognize him, do not give him the pet. If he is truly the owner, he will appreciate your precaution and return with the necessary information.

If you can't keep the lost pet at your home, take him to an animal shelter. You may consider checking on the pet in a few days to see if he's been claimed. If the pet is scheduled to be destroyed, you could perform a mission of mercy and help him get adopted. Perhaps this is the fates telling you it's time for another pet in your life.

11 Weather Tips

It is critical to be aware of how weather affects a pet's health and well-being. A pet left out on a very cold day can be struck by hypothermia or frostbite. On a hot day, the unattended pet could suffer from heat stroke. Both can be life-threatening conditions.

Stormy Weather

Storms are scary. The roar of the thunder, the illuminated sky — it's straight out of a horror flick. There are a few things that can be done to help calm a pet during storms. Draw curtains or close blinds to hide lightning. Drown out the noise of thunder with music, air-conditioner, or television.

Cold Weather

Pets should be introduced to cold weather for short intervals at a time. Allow them to gradually get used to it before sending them out to trek the frigid tundra. Don't ever leave pets outside without shelter for extended periods of time in cold weather. This, along with leaving a pet in the car, can lead to hypothermia. If pets are wet or damp, do not let them out until they are dry. If the wind chill drops below 20 degrees, keep short-haired or small pets inside the house. Remember the less body weight and hair a pet has, the less protection he has against the elements.

When pets are going to be outside for a while, make sure they have fresh water (not ice) and an enclosed shelter to protect them from wind, snow, and rain. A shelter is most beneficial to your pet when it is elevated from the ground so moisture does not gather. A door or cover goes a long way in blocking out the elements and keeping your pet warm. Furnish the outdoor shelter with things your pet can snuggle into such as blankets, towels, warming pads, pillows, or even hay.

If the weather is harsh, bring pets inside the house. If your pet has been exposed to salt on the streets or sidewalks, rinse their paws right away. Feed them more than you would normally because they need more energy and will be burning it quicker. Instead of bathing your pet in water, dry clean him by sprinkling baby powder or corn starch on his fur, then brushing out thoroughly.

When you get into your car each morning, knock on the hood a few times or honk the horn to alert animals who may be making their winter home in your engine. Be aware that antifreeze is deadly to animals. If you spill antifreeze, clean it up right away so your pet or the neighborhood animals do not ingest it.

Hot Weather

The keys to preventing overheating are access to shade and water. Bring your pets inside on those sweltering days. As you step outside, ask yourself how you'd feel in a fur coat today.

If you take your pet in the car with you, be aware of the temperature in the back seat. You may be comfortable with the air-conditioner aimed at you, but how hot is your pet in the back of your vehicle? Park in the shade and keep all the windows cracked. They should be open enough to allow fresh air in, but not so much that pet can get stuck trying to escape. Of course, windows open too wide can lead to a break-in resulting in a stolen pet or car. Set a bowl of water on the floor for your pet to drink while you're away. Remember that even on mild days, the sun can warm a closed car quickly. On a hot day, a closed car can reach deadly temperatures in minutes which can kill a pet. For this reason, NEVER leave your pet in a closed car on a hot day!

Be aware that a pet's fur acts as an insulator to heat as well as cold. Shaving your pets fur may sound like a good idea but could leave him vulnerable to the direct attack of the sun on his skin, as well as prevent him from cooling down.

Prevent burned pads by avoiding overheated surfaces. Protect your pet's nose and ears with sunscreen; they sunburn too. Use only pet-approved topical tanning lotions.

In addition to lots of water, give your pet ice cubes to munch on.

See the EMERGENCY CARE section on what to do if your pet is suffering from heat stroke.

12 Photographing Your Pet

The keys to a successful photo session with your pet are patience, praise, and a sense of humor. Have fun and enjoy the photo session. Your pet will appreciate your sense of humor.

Before the photo session, give your pet a good brushing. Clean your pet's eyes and ears so that he'll look his very best for the camera.

Begin by recruiting someone to help. The assistant's job is to help get your pet into the proper poses and keep him there. This is much easier said than done. Remember patience. Toys and treats can be used to get your pet's attention.

Be ready to shoot quickly when the pose is struck.

Keep the session short.

If your pet is the primary subject, he should fill at least half the frame.

Select a background that compliments your pet. Do not use a busy background that overwhelms your pet. A backdrop can be created by draping or hanging a towel or sheet behind your pet on a door, sofa, or wall.

Shoot at pet's level. This may mean getting down on hands and knees. Or, a small pet could be elevated by placing on a chair or table.

To reduce red eyes, avoid shooting your pet looking directly at camera. Try shooting pet at an angle. Avoid using a flash.

When shooting outside, avoid bright sun and shoot instead in bright shade. The objective is to avoid dark shadows on pet. Position the pet so that the light hits him on the side; this will flatter his fur and face.

13 Choosing a New Pet

So, you're thinking about getting a new pet. And why not? They're wonderful companions, love you unconditionally, and are as cute as can be. Like any relationship though, one should carefully consider this long-term commitment and closely examine your reasons for wanting a pet. Are you ready to assume responsibility for a pet for the next 10 to 20 years, or, have you thought that far ahead? Are you ready for the challenges of pet parenthood — or have you just thought about the fun stuff? Do you see your pooch as an addition to the family — or no more than a live alarm system?

Are You Ready For A Pet?

As a perspective pet parent, there are many things to consider before bringing a new pet home.

Time

Does your family's lifestyle leave room for daily walks, play, and care? Will you have time to make sure your pet keeps all veterinary appointments?

Cost

Can you afford the substantial cost to care for your pet? Food, toys, pet supplies, grooming, health, and dental care can add up quickly. If you're considering a large dog, realize that caring for a large dog is significantly more expensive than a smaller pet. Because of size and quantity, food, medication, pet supplies, and toys are more expensive for a large dog. You can expect to spend at least $400 a year for a cat and, depending on the dog, it could range from $500 to over $1,200 a year. In addition, there will be unexpected medical expenses. If you travel, there will be pet-sitting or boarding expenses.

Space

Do you have the space in your home to accommodate a pet? Where will your new pet sleep? Most pets prefer to sleep with you. Is there room in your bedroom for his bed? Where's the doggie diner? How about the kitty cafe? Small pets may be comfortable in a small apartment. However, most big dogs will require larger spaces to play, sleep, and exercise. Where will the pet bathroom(s) be located? Do you have a yard for pets to spend a little leisure time? How close are you to a park? Where will you exercise your pet?

Indoor/Outdoor

Will your pet be an indoor pet, outdoor pet, or have indoor and outdoor access? Some new dog owners believe dogs belong only in the backyard, but this rarely, if ever, works out well. A bored dog will soon look for ways to pass the time. Building a new deck and planting marigolds are not the constructive ideas they come up with. They usually occupy time with barking, chewing, digging, and escaping. Because they haven't gotten the attention needed, many backyard pets end up at the animal shelters. If you intend on keeping your dog outside, please consider a buddy for your pet. An outdoor pet will not require walks to relieve himself; however, he will still require daily attention, exercise, and playtime with you. Dogs are pack animals and are happiest in the company of others. Solitary confinement is a horrible sentence for them.

For kitty's sake, if possible, keep him safe by keeping him indoors. Because of all the potential dangers outdoors like cars, dogs, wildlife, other cats, and diseases, an outdoor cat has a much shorter expected lifespan. Many cat owners have found ways to bring the excitement and adventure of the outdoors inside. Kitty can now stalk a mechanical mouse or chase a feather toy with the same vigor as she would the real thing. Placing bird feeders in strategic window locations can also add hours of entertainment for kitty.

Landlord Approval

Remember that episode of "I Love Lucy' when the Ricardos had to hide their puppy from Fred Mertz because no pets were allowed in the building? In the end, the pooch was discovered, but Fred changed his policy because little Ricky named the dog after him. Well, that was television. In real life, you and Fred Mutts would be outta luck. Get approval from your landlord first.

Family Members

How do other members of your family feel about a new pet? Are they willing to pitch in to help care for the pet? Is anyone allergic to pet hair or dander? Will other pets accept the newcomer?

Patience/Supervision

Bringing home a new pet is similar to bringing home a two-year-old that will require constant supervision until it understands the house rules. Do you have the patience to make it through the adjustment and training period which, depending on the pet, could be months, maybe years? This may even require professional help from obedience trainers, behavior specialists, or veterinarians.

Responsibility

In the majority of households, it's mom who's left holding the doggie bag. Your kids will be convincing when they promise they will be the pet's primary care givers. They're not lying — they honestly believe what they're telling you. Don't you, though. You're the grown-up. Separate fact from fiction and realize that the kids will throw bones, play catch, and pet the animals. You will disinfect urine stains, rid fleas, and vacuum endless hair. How tolerant will you be of this additional work?

What Kind of Pet?

Okay, you've reviewed the rewards and challenges of pet parenthood and have decided to go ahead and adopt a cat or dog. Congratulations! Pet parenthood has its responsibilities, but it can also be an endless source of joy.

But wait, you've still got a few more items to consider

before picking out a name and food dish. Cat or dog? Male or female? Big or small? Active or mellow? Consider the following:

Cat or Dog

There's the obvious size difference between cats and dogs. With the exception of toy dog breeds, cats are usually smaller. While dogs want to be your constant companion, cats tend to be more independent. Dogs require daily attention to walk, feed, exercise, and play. In contrast, cats can tolerate being left alone for longer periods of time and don't require walks. On the other hand, dogs think you're the greatest thing since sliced beef, while cats secretly think you're the servant who brings the sliced beef.

The Gender Thing

There is no personality difference between male and female pets who have been spayed or neutered. Females tend to be smaller than males. Whichever sex you decide on, plan to have your pet "fixed." Unneutered males will fight, spray, and experience frustration, while unspayed females are messy and will yowl an incessant mating call while in heat bringing (spraying) males right to your door.

Size

Cats tend to be relatively close in size. But, there are always those few that exceed standards. Size becomes a much bigger issue for dogs. So, if you're thinking about getting a dog consider what size dog suits your family's lifestyle? Do you have a big yard and a station wagon? Or, are you in a studio apartment in the city? If you have small children, consider that a larger dog could accidentally hurt your child. Equally possible is that your child could accidentally injure a small pet. On the other hand, we've seen plenty of big dogs who play gently with children and hysterical toy breed dogs we wouldn't leave alone with a donut — let alone our children. What size dog can you control? If you're considering a puppy that will be large when full grown, will you and other family members have the strength to control him? Also, keep in mind there is a direct correlation between the size of a dog and the size of potential problems. Where a small dog may chew a furniture leg, a large dog may destructively chew an entire sofa in an afternoon.

Dominant vs. Submissive

Think about the kind of people you like to hang out with. Are they big personalities or a little mellow? You'll probably want a pet who's a lot like your buddies. And what type of pet would be happiest in your home? Would your busy household be a frightening place for the shy submissive? Do you have the energy to keep up with your bold and curious little dominant?

Hair type

We don't mean put your dog's hair in a sweet little ribbon. In fact, please don't. It looks silly and other dogs will tease little Bergdorf. But do consider climate, grooming, and shedding in your decision whether to choose a long or short-hair pet. If you're not into high maintenance, then consider a short-hair pet.

Energy Level

Do you want a pet who's energetic and playful? Or gentle and calm? Some breeds are known for certain temperaments. The age of your pet will also be a factor in whether your pet wants to play ball or just watch a ballgame on TV.

Number of Pets

Consider two pets. Now, Noah also subscribed to the two pet theory, but for very different reasons. Since your spayed and neutered pets won't be reproducing anyway, we suggest two pets because they'll keep each other company. Coupled pets are happier and tend to be less destructive than a pet left home alone.

Age

For many reasons, we highly recommend considering an adult adoption. The most compelling reason is that adult pets are less likely to be adopted so you would be saving a pet. Adults are less expensive (they've already gone through all the baby vaccinations and teething stage). What you see is what you get - size, personality, and appearance. Many times they are already house-trained and may have some obedience training. They're less fragile and more mature — a perfect combination for a household with young children. Patience and understanding will insure family bonding. You may have to work with some old habits, but teaching an older dog new tricks is easier than rumored.

Perhaps you have your heart set on a puppy or kitten. It's hard not to fall in love with those adorable sweet little bundles of energy. Raising a young pet allows owners to play an active role in shaping the pet's behavior. Pet "childhood" is a whirlwind of activity. They require constant supervision as they chew, scratch, whine, bite, and investigate everything through childhood. They've got a lot to learn and will need you to teach them. Right now, they're cute little ones; sometimes it's difficult to predict how their looks and personality will develop. Pets should be at least eight weeks old before going to a new home. They will need the first of many veterinary visits to begin immediately.

Tips for Adopting a Pet

You may be asking yourself how in the world to figure all of this out before adopting a pet. It's easy enough to ask the breed, gender, and age. And it's easy enough to see the pet's size and hair type. But how do you figure out if a pet's active, submissive, independent, or sociable? Observe the pet for a while. See how she acts with the others. Note whether she seems friendly toward you or indifferent. When you approach the pet, is she curious and eager to make friends? Or is she shaking nervously, curled up in a ball under furniture? Be aware of clues pets give you regarding who they are and what they'll be like at home. However, if you're planning on adopting from a shelter, realize that the pet is in a stressful environment and will most likely not be himself. Once at home, you will probably see a new confident, relaxed, happy pet develop.

Where to Find a Pet

Because of the overpopulation of pets, there is an abundance of pets looking for good homes. Wonderful pets in need of homes can be found at local animal shelters and breed rescue groups.

Animal Shelters

Many special pets are waiting for homes at local animal shelters. Adopting a pet from an animal shelter not only saves a pet from possible death, but also makes room for another needy pet. Thousands of pets are abandoned each year because of negligence on an owner's part to care for and train their pet. When observing dogs at the animal shelter, remember that they are stressed, frightened, and lonely in this environment. Be patient and spend time with them to determine if they are the right one for you.

Choosing a New Pet 129

Pets from the shelters will require sensitivity, love, and a lot of attention to help them with the transition. All pets adopted from shelters will have already been spayed or neutered.

San Diego Animal Shelters

Closed Sundays, Mondays, & Holidays

Central County Animal Shelter (619) 236-4250
5480 Gaines Street, San Diego

North County Animal Shelter (619) 438-2312
2481 Palomar Airport Road, Carlsbad

South County Animal Shelter (619) 263-7741
5821 Sweetwater Road, Bonita

Other Shelters in San Diego Area

Camp Pendleton Animal Shelter (619) 725-4003
Building 25132, Camp Pendleton

Chula Vista Animal Shelter (619) 691-5123
690 Otay Valley Road, Chula Vista

Coronado Animal Shelter (619) 522-7371
578 Orange Avenue, Coronado

El Cajon Animal Shelter (619) 441-1580
1275 North Marshall Avenue, El Cajon

Escondido Humane Society (619) 745-4362
3000 Las Palmas Avenue, Escondido

North County Humane Society & SPCA (619)757-4357
2905 San Luis Rey Road, Oceanside

Private Shelters that do not accept Strays

Helen Woodward Animal Center   (619) 756-3791
6461 El Apajo, Rancho Santa Fe

Rancho Coastal Humane Society   (619) 753-6413
389 Requeza Street, Encinitas

San Diego Humane Society   (619) 299-7012
887 Sherman Street, San Diego

Friends of Cats   (619) 561-0361
15587 Olde Highway 80, El Cajon

National Cat Protection Society   (619) 469-8771
9031 Birch Street, Spring Valley

Breed Rescue Groups

These groups are devoted to the well-being of specific breeds. Each year, thousands of purebreds are abandoned or turned in to shelters by their owners. Unlike human athletes, retired racing dogs do not look forward to lucrative product endorsements or careers in sports-casting. Instead, a greyhound might spend his retirement years with your family, regaling you with stories of his golden years on the track. A rescue group exists for almost every breed of dog. Similar to animal shelters, all pets adopted through breed rescue groups will already have been spayed or neutered.

If you are interested in adopting a specific breed that is not on the following list, ask your local veterinarian, animal shelter, breeder or dog show sponsor where to find that rescue group. Many of the breed rescue groups can be found listed on the World Wide Web.

Choosing a New Pet

Local Breed Rescue Groups

Airedale Terrier	(619) 744-5171
Anatolian Shepherd Dog	(619) 445-3334
Australian Cattle Dog	(619) 723-8092
Australian Shepherd	(800) 892-ASCA
Basset Hound	(619) 286-8638
Beagle	(619) 443-2149
Bichon Frise	(619) 751-1132
Bulldog	(619) 447-9711
Boxer	(619) 747-5712
Cairn Terrier	(619) 728-7133
Dachshund	(619) 475-7738
Dalmation	(619) 667-2020
Doberman Pinscher	(619) 443-8944
Fox Terrier	(619) 464-5454
German Shorthair Pointer	(619) 726-4813
German Shepherd	(619) 447-6963
Golden Retriever	(619) 698-3830
Gordon Setter	(619) 222-3735
Great Pyrenees	(619) 788-6799
Greyhound	(619) 443-0940
Irish Setter	(909) 676-4436
Jack Russell Terrier	(619) 271-8933
Labrador Retriever	(619) 445-8115
Lhasa Apso	(619) 278-2484
Mastiff	(619) 448-7790
Miniature Poodle	(619) 758-7322
Miniature Schnauzer	(619) 661-6444
Newfoundland	(619) 448-8848
Norwegian Elkhound	(619) 444-7133
Norwich Terrier	(619) 744-5171
Old English Sheepdog	(805) 221-5004
Papillon	(619) 751-1277
Rottweiler	(619) 445-8309
Saluki	(619) 723-7231
Scottish Terrier	(714) 893-5821
Shetland Sheepdog	(800) 574-3584

Shih Tzu	(619) 942-0874
Standard Poodle	(619) 758-7322
Tibetan Mastiff	(619) 543-1166
Toy Fox Terrier	(619) 731-2339
Toy Poodle	(619) 758-7322
Vizsla	(714) 493-8403
West Highland Terrier	(619) 755-6521
Welsh Corgi (Cardigan)	(619) 670-1147
Welsh Corgi (Pembroke)	(619) 480-8348
Welsh Terrier	(619) 744-5171
Whippet	(619) 477-4222
Pug	(619) 685-3580

Choosing a New Pet

Questions to Ask About an Adoptive Pet

Many people handling the adoption of pets will not have all the answers to your questions, or the information they have may be inaccurate. Nonetheless, it's a good idea to ask anyway.

1. Does the pet get along with others: children, men, women, other cats or dogs?
2. Is the pet house trained or obedience trained?
3. What kind of temperament does the pet have? Is it fearful or aggressive?
4. Does the pet need special care?
5. Does this pet or its breed have certain health or medical needs?

When pets are abandoned, their former owners usually did not take the time and give the attention needed, or they may be the victim of circumstance. His owner may have died, divorced, moved, or had a baby. Perhaps a new landlord does not allow pets. Abandoned pets will need extra patience, attention, and training. Pets are not themselves at the shelters. Take them outside and give them a chance to calm down and get to know you. As she spends more time with you in a quieter, relaxed environment, you will see her confidence grow and personality shine through.

Pet Pages

14 New Pet Care

Bringing home a new pet will require some preparation. Planning ahead will help insure a smooth transition for you and your new pet. This chapter will help you plan for those first few weeks with your new pet.

Prior to picking up your new pet, make an appointment with your veterinarian for the pet's first visit. If you have other pets at home, you may want to see your veterinarian first before taking your pet home.

Pet Supplies

Before bringing your new pet home, plan a shopping trip to pick up necessary pet supplies.

- Premium Nutrition Pet Food:

    Abrupt changes in pet food can cause stomach upset and diarrhea. To avoid this problem, gradually mix new pet food with the old pet food so your pet can slowly become accustomed to the new food.

- Nutritious Pet Treats

- Food and Water Bowls:

    Untippable, porcelain, or stainless steel are recommended. Placing a mat under the bowls may help contain stray kibbles and water puddles.

- Collar (Avoid using a choke collar for everyday use):

    Two fingers should fit between the collar and neck. Be sure to check fit regularly as pet grows. For cats, look for a strangle-proof, breakaway, or elastic sectioned collar.

- Identification Tags:

    If your pet should get lost or injured, an identification tag is his best bet for finding his way home. People who find your pet will return him to you instead of taking him to the animal shelter or keeping him as their new pet. If the pet is injured, a vet is more likely to treat a pet with tags. Unfortunately, tags on collars can be removed either purposely or by accident. To safeguard your pet, in addition to tags, you may also wish to have your pet tattooed or have a small identification microchip inserted. Your vet can inject the microchip between your pet's shoulder blades without any pain to the pet. Before microchipping your pet, contact your local animal shelters to find out if they scan for microchips and, if so, ask which manufacturer's chips they scan.

- Carrier or Crate

- Odor and Stain Removers:

    Even with adult adoptions, you will have mistakes. So, the best plan is to have supplies on hand when the need arises.

- Safe Toys:

    Toys serve as playthings, boredom eliminators, and provide "teething" comfort for young pets. There are many toys available for dogs and cats. Please consider safety when purchasing toys. Similar to buying toys for children, avoid toys with squeakers, foam, those that can be swallowed, or toys with strings that a pet can become entangled in.

- Repellent or Chew Stops:

    These products will help you keep kitty from dining on your favorite plant or puppy from nibbling on your furnishings.

- Grooming Supplies (shampoo, combs, brushes):

    Talk with your veterinarian or groomer about the specific grooming supplies needed for your new pet.

- Washable, Durable Bed:

    A comfortable bed for your pet will help you and your pet sleep better. Trust me, when he's up, you will be too.

- Rescue Stickers that indicate the number and type of pets for entrances to your home.

- Litter and Litter Box (for cats):

    Ask the previous owner what type of box and litter the cat was using. Any changes to box or litter type should be done gradually. The goal is to gain cat's acceptance; sudden changes may send him looking for another spot.

- Scratching Post (for cats):

    Look for a sturdy post that doesn't sway or won't easily tip over. It should be tall enough for your cat to fully stretch and scratch.

- Baby gates (for dogs):

    Baby gates are great for confining new dogs, preferably in areas with scrubbable floors. From a dog's perspective, he will be happier behind a gate that he can see through rather than a door that shuts him off from you.

Pet-Proofing Your Home

Next, take the time to walk through your home and pet-proof any possible dangers. Much like bringing a child into your home, you will need to make provisions for your pet's safety. Get down on your hands and knees and look for poisons, small or sharp objects, and other possible dangers.

New pets will sniff, lick, chew, tug, push, and bat anything they come across. They will jump and crawl into anything that seems of interest. Some are even pretty good at using their paws to open doors and cabinets.

Please be vigilant in removing hazards. Here are some hazards to be aware of:

- All medications, poisons, cleaning products, and anything else that would be harmful if ingested, should be locked away from pet's access.
- Remove valuables or breakables.
- Remove tablecloths or your new pet may end up pulling it off for you.

New Pet Care

- Make sure that trash cans are not accessible.

- Never leave plastic bags out; a curious pet can quickly find themselves entangled and might suffocate.

- Remove drapery cords, string, yarn, and thread from pet's reach. These are dangerous if swallowed or entangled.

- Keep windows and stairway doors closed to prevent possible falls.

- Keep an eye on reclining chairs; small pets can get caught in the inner mechanism.

- Never leave pet unattended in kitchen with hot stove-top surfaces.

- Check dryer before turning on; cats have been known to hop into dryers for a little cat nap.

- Check with your veterinarian or local nursery about safe indoor and outdoor plants. Many plants are harmful and some even fatal for pets.

- Protect pet from chewing on electrical cords. Move cords out of pet's reach, use repellents, or use protective coverings on cords to prevent electrical shock. Always supervise your pet in areas with electrical cords.

Outdoor areas need to be pet-proofed as well. Take a walk around the outside of your home and look for possible dangers.

- Remove any antifreeze drippings.

- Store any poisons, pesticides, and other deadly products out of pet's reach.

- If possible, remove or cover wires, ropes, or cords that pet may chew or become entangled in.

- Walk fence-line and look for any possible escape areas and repair.
- Be sure your fence is tall enough to prevent an aerial escape.

What to Expect ... the Good, the Bad, & the Ugly

You've probably already thought about all the **Good** stuff that comes from a new pet. There's the unconditional love, companionship, entertainment, and their playful spirit. These are probably the reasons you've chosen a pet.

Expect some **Bad** as in bad behavior, which may include barking, biting, yowling, scratching, chewing, just to name a few examples. Now, to your pet, what we call bad behavior may be perfectly normal and acceptable cat or dog behavior. But, as his human companions, we may find their behavior totally unacceptable. You will need to show him what is good versus bad behavior. He will not know the difference until you take time to show him.

Don't forget about the **Ugly**. This is the term used to describe all those surprises your pet will leave you like urine, vomit, spills, or broken possessions. No pet owner escapes these surprises. Count on it; you too will be gifted with these types of surprises.

As a new puppy parent, expect some chewed-up stuff, house training errors, and lots of puppy energy. Your puppy will probably be eager to sniff, chew, run, and investigate everything. You'll also get a chance to hear his vocal skills with a repertoire of barks, yowls, and whining. Some pets initially may be shy or confused. This is normal. With time, patience and consistency, your pet will fully adapt to his new environment.

From Miss Kitty, you can expect a flurry of activity — jumping, climbing, tumbling, and scratching are part

New Pet Care

of her routine. She'll chase her tail, never realizing the futility of this pursuit. She'll decide that your telephone cord is her mortal enemy and do battle with this spiral monster daily. Dull moments are rare in a house with a new kitten. During those quiet times, Miss Kitty will be curled up on the sunny spot of the floor, dreaming of a trip to the all-you-can-eat sushi bar.

The following is a 10-point plan to help maximize the good and minimize the bad and ugly:

1. **Give lots of love** and attention to your new pet. Be patient with him and forgive his inevitable mistakes. Take the time to enjoy your pet's homecoming and help him adjust to his new home. It is time well spent.

2. **Spend time at home** with your new pet, allowing him the opportunity to get used to his new environment. Respect his need for peace and quiet and resist the urge to over-handle.

3. **Take him on a guided tour** of your home right away. Show him his bed or crate, food and water bowls, and bathroom area.

4. **Ease pet's transition with the familiar.** This can be done by bringing a towel or blanket from pet's first home to his new place. Feed pet what he's used to eating, slowly mixing it with new food. For cats, use the same cat litter that it's used to.

5. **Confine pet to a room** with an adult present. It's better to catch house training errors before, instead of after, they happen. If possible, keep your pet in a room with washable floors. This room should have food and water bowls and access to the bathroom area. For kitty, this means having the litter box in the room. For puppy, this means a paper area or access to outdoors to relieve himself.

   It's best to keep new cats confined for a few weeks

until they are familiar with their new environment. This way you won't lose your new friend, and she won't lose sight of those very necessary items like the litter box.

6. **Put new pet on a schedule**. This schedule should include time for meals, bathroom duties (for dogs), play, and sleep. While this may seem as rigid as pet boot camp, a routine will help your new pet adjust to its new home.

7. **Place bed or crate in the bedroom** of the person responsible for pet care. This is necessary for puppies so that the responsible person can take an awakened puppy out in middle of night to go to the bathroom. Being close to people will help him adjust to his new home away from littermates. A hot water bottle and blanket might be comforting to a puppy. Your new cat may prefer to sleep on your bed. If you don't want her on your bed, then you will need to provide her with an alternative that is agreeable to her.

8. **Visit the veterinarian** to ensure your pet is healthy and vaccinated on time.

9. **Socialization is an important part** of a puppy or kitten's development. Provide lots of opportunities for your new pet to meet others. Show him off; he'll love the attention and who can resist a puppy or kitten. Puppies should remain at home until about sixteen weeks of age, and they are done with their early vaccinations. After that, they should be ready to meet the world. By introducing your pet to new people and situations, you help to boost your pet's confidence. This is especially important for timid pets.

10. **Have fun with your new pet.** Let him know you think he's wonderful to spend time with. Make time every day to play. You and your pet will love it.

How to Crate Train Your Dog

Like humans, dogs want a special place that's all their own. Kids build tree houses; adults invest in real estate. Our four-legged furry friends are no different. Giving your puppy a crate helps him feel safe and secure. Crates can be used as a house-breaking aid, a safe place for your pet, or for car or airline travel.

1. Select a crate that is big enough for pet to stand up, turn around, and lay down stretched out on his side. For puppies, there are crates available that expand with a dog's growth.

2. To begin training, leave the crate door open and put treats inside to reward puppy for going in. Make this a comfortable retreat for pet by placing a blanket and chew toys inside. Encourage pet to explore his new crate. Allow him to come and go at his own pace.

3. Once he is familiar with his crate, shut the crate door for a few minutes. Gradually build up the time spent in the shut crate.

4. The crate can be used for nighttime sleeping, daytime rest periods, and times when pet can't be supervised. Limit the time your pet is confined to the crate. He shouldn't be confined for hours on end or for the rest of his life. The crate should be used as a training tool and resting place, not a prison. Be sensitive to bathroom breaks by limiting the amount of time spent in the crate. Allow at least an hour break between crate shut-ins.

5. Once puppy is house trained, leave the crate door open. You'll find him choosing his crate as his resting spot when he's tired.

Don't

- get a crate that's too big
- force puppy inside crate

- worry that puppy will use crate to relieve himself; puppies have an instinctive desire to keep their crate's clean
- leave puppy in crate all day
- make the crate a punishing place; his crate should not be associated with fear or punishment.

House Training Your Puppy

House training can be fun and rewarding for both you and puppy. Well . . . maybe that's stretching it, but it doesn't have to be a major trauma either. It will take discipline and commitment, but the effort is well worth it. You know the consequences — enough said.

Creating a Routine

Establish routines with your new puppy, like taking walks at the same time every day. Good times to schedule walks are first thing in the morning, after puppy's meals and naps, and last thing before sleep. Take puppy to a designated spot for relief. (This is known as the L'Plaza du Pupu, if you have a poodle.) While a set routine is optimal, watch for signs that puppy needs to go. Don't ignore telltale signs such as sniffing, whining, turning in circles, and going to the door. In canine, this clearly translates to "Hurry up, I've gotta go!"

Your puppy depends on you for scheduled walks. The following chart helps identify how often puppy should be walked.

Puppy Age	Walk Puppy every...
6 weeks	4 hours
8 weeks	5 hours
12 weeks	6 hours
5-6 months	8 hours

If puppy doesn't relieve himself in 10 minutes, bring him inside and try again later. Don't play with him until after he relieves himself.

Teach phrases like "hurry up" and praise him when he does. Reward puppy's success by lavishing him with praise. You may be tempted to let puppy find a private place to go to on his own, but during training, you should supervise and keep him on his leash.

When you are not at home to supervise, try to keep puppy on washable floors. Set-off an area with a baby gate and make sure puppy has a space of his own like a crate or bed.

Avoiding Mistakes

Let's face it, puppy mistakes are no fun to deal with. In fact, they stink. But remember, puppies don't have mistakes in the house out of anger or stupidity. They do so because they haven't been taught otherwise. Accidents are human error, not puppy spite. If you think your pooch is trying to tell you he doesn't like you by messing on your carpet, you're wrong.

If you catch puppy in the middle of a mistake, startle him with a loud noise and take him to his outdoor spot. Never correct or punish after the fact. And by all means, don't rub puppy's face in his mistake. It doesn't teach him anything except fear, and it's just plain mean. If you find a mistake, simply clean it up and go on with the day. It is too late to make a fuss. There are a number of products on the market designed to clean and neutralize odors. In a pinch, a mixture of water and vinegar solution can be used to neutralize the odor. Never use ammonia; it will act as a magnet for puppy to "mark" that spot again.

Be sure to give puppy a "last call" before bedtime. If you have a very young puppy, be sensitive to signs of restlessness. Your puppy may not be able to make it through the night without another trip to the puppy rest stop. If you hear him moving about, take him out. Remember this is not playtime. Take him outside and then right back to bed. Otherwise, he may decide it's fun to wake you up each night for a little late evening play. If you're a sound sleeper, then set your alarm for 4 or 5 hours and take puppy outside.

After puppy is 4-5 months old, he should be house trained and making few mistakes. If problems persist, ask your veterinarian to check for bladder infection or any other medical problem.

Puppies are eager to please and make you happy. By reinforcing good behavior and patiently redirecting mistakes, both puppy and you can soon establish a routine that keeps both of you happy. Then, you can move on to something really fun like chasing Frisbees™.

Pet Health Signs

You vowed to love your pet in sickness and in health, but how do you tell the difference? The language barrier poses a challenge to communications with your pet, but you can tell if she's not feeling well by observing physical signs and her demeanor. If you

New Pet Care

see any signs of illness or unusual behavior, contact your veterinarian.

In Sickness...	And in Health...
Lifeless, runny eyes	Energetic, bright, shiny eyes
Runny or dry nose	Clean, wet, cool nose
Dull or uneven coat with a lot of shedding baldness, dandruff or matting	Glossy, full coat
Scratching	Not scratching
Ears red, smelly or filled with black, waxy substance	Clean, pink ears
Listless, unsociable	Energetic, alert and playful
Soft, runny or bloody stool	Firm stool
Thin but pot-bellied (may be worms)	Well proportioned body
Limps	Doesn't limp
Doesn't eat	Has good appetite
Cries in pain	Seems happy
Scaly, scabby or red skin	Smooth, flexible skin

Diary of a Puppy in a New Home

Dear Diary,

Today we went to the park for a picnic and played this really neat game where someone throws a ball to me, I catch it in my mouth, slobber all over it, and bring it back to do it all over again.

I had a good time and am adjusting to my new life with the furless, dry-nosed, two-leggers quite well. I love the family's two children, but am having a little difficulty with the younger one, Lloyd.

When Mom and Dad sprung me from the animal shelter, they showed little David and Lloyd how to approach me, holding their hands extended so I could get a good sniff and speaking to me in a soft gentle voice. They showed both boys how to pet me, pick me up, put me down, and let me sit in their laps. I know they've been trained, so I just can't understand why four-year-old Lloyd is so rough while his eleven-year-old brother handles me just fine.

Frankly, I feel a bit distressed by the fact that Lloyd seems to treat me like a toy, not a living thing, much less a member of the family. He picks me up by the scruff of the neck, pulls on my tail, chases me, drops me on the ground, teases me, and sometimes even hits me. Furthermore, I'm getting a little cranky 'cause every time I try to take a nap around this place, Lloyd starts yanking at my ears. When I go to my food bowl, there's Lloyd, ready to make my life difficult.

I really love the kid; I just wish his older brother or parents would spend a little more time redirecting his behavior. David seems to have the routine down pat. He's gentle, loving, and kind. Most importantly, he lets me be. He's quite a kid. I even see him wash his hands after handling me to avoid contact with any possible parasites I may have. (I'm so embarrassed!!)

Momma-furless is going to bring home a new baby soon, and I've already been briefed as to how we're going to handle the homecoming (okay, I overheard it, so what?!). First, they're going to bring me a piece of baby's clothing so I can get a good whiff of the little tike. Then, they're going to put me on my leash and let me approach the little cutie, since I already know my obedience commands. I can hardly wait. I've always wanted a pet baby!

I think I smell a burger on the grill. Until tomorrow,

Corky ✗

Consider Alternatives to Declawing

Instead of declawing your pet, why not take the time to direct your cat's natural scratching instinct to an appropriate place like a cat tree or scratching post? Declawing is a painful and costly surgical procedure which removes the first joint of a cat's toe and its surrounding tissue. The recovery is painful and can be lengthy. There is a risk of infection, hemorrhage, or regrowth. Typically, only the front paws are declawed which leaves a cat dependent on her hind claws. Declawing leaves outdoor cats virtually defenseless against attack from other animals. If you adopt a cat who is already declawed, keep her indoors.

Some cats experience behavior changes such as biting and growling. Because of the pain and risk involved, many veterinarians will not perform this procedure. Britain and a few other countries have made declawing illegal.

Take time to show your cat which places she may scratch as well as correcting her when she scratches areas that are not acceptable. When you catch kitty scratching furniture, tell her "No," firmly and give her a quick squirt of water.

Cat Trees/Scratching Posts - Provide a sturdy place for your cat to scratch. Make sure it is tall enough for her to scratch and is secured so it doesn't tip over. Cat trees sprinkled with a little cat nip make the area even more inviting. After you catch kitty scratching where she shouldn't, direct her attention to the scratching post. Tantalize her with toys or yarn. When she scratches the tree, reward your kitty with praise and a treat. Your cat will soon learn that scratching the couch leads to correction, but scratching the post leads to reward.

Trim Claws — Keep your cat's claws trimmed and smooth. See GROOMING section for tips on trimming claws.

Don't Use Hands as Toys — By teasing kitty with your hands or fingers, you are training her to scratch and bite you.

Cover Nails — New plastic nail covers are now available to temporarily guard your family and furniture from scratches while you are training kitty to use her cat tree. These are similar to press-on nails for humans that can be applied by you or your veterinarian.

The Kitty Litter

When introducing a new kitten or cat to his litter box, use the same brand of litter that he's accustomed to. If you would like to use another brand, gradually mix litters over a period of time. An abrupt change in litter can send kitty looking for another place to relieve himself. Cats are darned serious about that litter. Don't mess around or they might.

Litter Options

There are many different types of cat litters from which to choose, but ultimately the choice is kitty's. If he does not like the brand you've selected, urinating elsewhere is his veto. If this occurs, try other brands until he is satisfied.

Flushable — The benefits are obvious — you scoop, you drop, you flush. Simple as that.

Clumping — This litter clumps urine spots so you can scoop away easily. The drawback is that litter can stick to paws that cats will ingest while grooming. The possible health hazards from ingesting litter are still being debated. Some say that it is harmful while others contend that there is no danger to cat's health.

Scented — It may be tempting to use scented litters that mask the urine odor, but resist. Some scents such as citrus can repel cats. You don't want kitty to mistake her litter box for a fruit basket, or she'll need to search elsewhere to do her business.

Litter Boxes

Cats are finicky about everything and litter boxes are no exception. If your household box does not pass his inspection, guess how he lets you know? You got it — he finds another place for his duties.

Scoop out litter box daily and always make sure the litter is fresh. Once a week, empty litter box and disinfect with bleach to prevent the breeding of germs that cause disease. Rinse thoroughly and leave outside to air out fumes. Avoid using pine-oil based products which are toxic to cats.

Each cat should have his own box. Large homes may

require several boxes, placed strategically throughout the house so that kitty is never too far from an appropriate spot for relief. Be sure to place litter boxes in easily accessible areas that are not highly trafficked. Cats need their privacy.

Indoor Cats

On average, indoor cats live three times longer than outdoor cats. Cats love the outdoors. And why not? They can run free, climb trees, and chase birds. But for their own good, keep them inside. Although they are smart, quick, and alert, they cannot defend themselves against all the dangers of the outside world.

A cat can lead a happy fulfilling life indoors as long as you provide lots of love, attention, and, of course, toys. Inside your home, a cat is protected from:

- cars
- disease & parasites
- unsealed poisons
- unfriendly animals
- mean people
- traps

15 Preventative Health Care

Wouldn't it be great if pets came with translating machines like the ones they use at the United Nations? You could place your earphones on and quickly understand that a certain high pitch meow means, "I have a lump in my ear that's causing me considerable pain." Since this nifty gadget doesn't exist, your pet depends on you to notice changes in health and seek veterinary care as needed.

In order to detect problems, you should become familiar with your pet's normal weight, behavior, and activity level. Notable changes in these areas should be a red flag that your pet is due for a trip to the veterinarian.

Inspect your pet's skin, eyes, ears, mouth, nose, paws, pads, and claws regularly. To make this more pleasurable for your pet, this can be done while petting or massaging the pet. The benefits of regular touching are three-fold. First, it will alert you early to any health problems — bumps, parasites, cuts, sores, or rashes. Second, it will help your pet become accustomed to being handled by people. And third, pets grow to enjoy the undivided attention. Have friends and family meet and handle your pets to help them become more comfortable with others. If the pet seems fearful or anxious, begin slowly by limiting the number of new people and the amount of time they spend with pet. Remember, the objective is to build up the pet's confidence, not to overwhelm him.

Massaging your pet is a wonderful addition to your health maintenance routine. Once a week, give your pet a head-to-tail massage, gently moving both hands circularly around face, ears, neck, sides, legs, and feet. This helps your pet's circulation and directs your attention to any changes on skin surface.

While weekly massage is an excellent method of detecting problems, be sure to give your pet the sight and sniff test as well. Closely examine ears, smelling for irregular odor. If your pet scratches her ears or shakes her head, there may be a problem. Check with your veterinarian.

As your family sets its annual budget, be sure to include regular veterinary care as well as unexpected medical costs. Your best bet for a healthy pet is making sure her health care needs are met in a timely manner. Don't cut corners by using human medication, unless your veterinarian specifically advises this. It is a dangerous experiment that could even be deadly for your pet.

Take your pet on car trips that don't lead to the veterinarian to avoid anxiety around the car. This is more commonly known as Toyotaphobia and can lead to many years of pet psychotherapy.

Finding the Right Veterinarian

The best way to find a veterinarian is to get a recommendation from someone you know and trust. If you are moving to a new city, ask your current veterinarian for a referral. You might also ask local animal welfare groups or shelters which local veterinarians volunteer their time. Doctors who provide free services to needy pets are likely to be in the profession for all the right reasons. You could also check with local breeders for a recommendation. Additionally, check medical societies and professional associations for membership as well as grievances or malpractice suits filed.

When you visit a veterinarian's office, ask if you may tour the facility. Note the cleanliness of the facility both by sight and smell. Is the staff friendly and helpful? Do they seem to genuinely care for pets and people?

Are you comfortable with how the veterinarian or staff answers your questions? Or do you feel rushed and unimportant? Do the other pets seem at ease? Or are two cats plotting their escape from cell block C? Is the office conveniently located for you? What are the office hours? And what is the policy for emergencies during hours when the facility is closed? Do they offer grooming or boarding services?

For the Anxious Cat

As a rule, a cat's hatred of car rides is second only to her hatred of veterinarian visits. Nonetheless, you should take her on short trips in her cat carrier to other places to help kitty get used to the car. Think of it as a vet drill. The more you practice, the less stressful a real trip to the veterinarian will seem.

If your pet is especially nervous about trips to the veterinarian, you may consider going during slower times (ask appointment scheduler), taking kitty to a cats-only veterinarian, or finding a veterinarian who makes house calls.

Alternative Medicine

Similar to human medicine, many pet owners are seeking alternative methods of care outside of traditional medicine. Some seek this out for ongoing, preventative care. Others go in search as a last resort.

When traditional medicine offers no hope of helping their beloved pet, many pet owners seek the assistance of an alternative health practitioner. If alternative medicine is unable to cure the pet, it may at least provide pain relief, improving the pet's quality of life. This approach may be used independent of or in conjunction with traditional veterinary care.

Holistic medicine treats the whole patient rather than just focusing on the area of discomfort. Body parts are not isolated, but instead seen as part of the entire living being. The veterinarian will try to determine what is going on in the pet's body as well as the pet's environment.

Less enlightened pets may tease yours and call her granola kitty, but holistic medicine is a well-respected and popular practice in most parts of the world. Some alternatives to traditional veterinary care in-

Preventative Health Care

clude acupuncture, Bach flower remedies, basic and therapeutic nutrition, herbs, laser therapy, massage, homeopathy, magnetic therapy, and chiropractic care.

For more information or to locate a holistic practitioner in your area, send a SASE (Self-Addressed Stamped Envelope) to the following contacts:

American Holistic Veterinary Medicine Association
2214 Old Emmorton Road
Bel Air, MD 21015
410-515-7774

American Veterinary Chiropractic Association
P.O. Box 249
Port Byron, IL 61275
309-523-3995

International Veterinary Acupuncture Society
2140 Conestoga Road
Chester Springs, PA 19425
610-827-7245

International Association for Veterinary Homeopathy
334 Knollwood Lane
Woodstock, GA 30188
770-516-5954

Academy for Veterinary Homeopathy
1283 Lincoln Street
Eugene, OR 97401
503-342-7665

Preventative Care

The key to good health care, alternative or traditional, is prevention and early intervention. Vaccinations and parasite control will prevent contagious or fatal diseases. Weekly handling and thorough inspection of eyes, ears, feet, skin, teeth, and paws will alert you to potential problems. If you notice sudden change in pet's weight, appetite, or overall demeanor, let your veterinarian know immediately.

Cats and dogs, like humans, can be protected by vaccination against many serious and potentially fatal diseases caused by bacteria and viruses.

Your veterinarian is your best source of advice regarding vaccinations and overall health of your pet. However, you are also an important source of information for your veterinarian. Be sure to tell your veterinarian about any special considerations that may have an effect on your pet's ability to respond to vaccines. These special circumstances could include stressful events, such as long car trips, exposure to sick animals, and changes in diet, sleeping, elimination, or other habits. Knowledge of these special circumstances, combined with a thorough examination of your pet, will help your veterinarian give your pet the best possible care.

According to the American Veterinary Medical Association, the following vaccinations are recommended for dogs and cats.

Recommended Canine Vaccinations

Recommended Canine Vaccinations

Date	DHLP*	Parvovirus	Bordatellosis	Rabies	Coronavirus

*Distemper, Hepatitis, Leptospirosis, Parainfluenza

Canine Diseases

Canine Distemper

This is a highly contagious viral disease transmitted by direct or indirect contact with the discharges from an infected dog's eyes or nose. A healthy dog does not need to come in direct contact with an infected dog because the virus can be carried by air currents and inanimate objects.

Early signs of canine distemper are similar to those of a severe cold and often go unrecognized by the pet owner. The respiratory problems may be accompanied by vomiting and diarrhea. A nervous system disorder may also develop. The death rate from canine distemper is greater than 50% in adult dogs and much higher in puppies. Even if the dog survives, distemper can cause permanent damage to a dog's nervous system, sense of smell, hearing, and sight. Partial or total paralysis is not uncommon.

Infectious Canine Hepatitis

This is caused by a virus that can infect many tissues, but usually attacks the liver causing hepatitis. In some instances, a whiteness or cloudiness of the eye may accompany the disease. Another strain of the same virus can cause respiratory tract infections. These viruses are transmitted by contact with objects that have been contaminated with the urine from infected dogs. Infectious Hepatitis is different from human hepatitis.

Canine Parvovirus (CPV)

This is a serious problem due to the highly resistant nature of the virus. CPV can withstand extreme temperature changes and exposure to most disinfectants. The source of the infection is usually dog feces which can contaminate cages, shoes, and can be carried on the feet and hair of infected animals.
This virus attacks the intestinal tract, white blood cells, and heart muscle. Clinical signs include vomiting, severe diarrhea, accompanied by a loss of appetite, depression, and high fever. Most deaths occur within 48-72 hours after the onset of clinical signs. Pups, less than 3 months of age, can experience an inflammation of the heart (myocarditis). Infected pups may act depressed, collapse gasping for

breath, and death may follow immediately. Pups that survive are likely to have permanently damaged hearts.

Canine Bordetellosis

This is caused by bacterium Bordetella Bronchiseptica which is present in the respiratory tracts of many animals. It is a primary cause of the severe chronic cough, tracheobronchitis (kennel cough). In addition to the cough, some dogs develop a purulent nasal discharge. Transmission most frequently occurs by contact with the nasal secretions of infected dogs.

Canine Parainfluenza

This is caused by a virus which produces a mild respiratory tract infection. It is often associated with other respiratory tract viruses. In combination, these viruses are usually transmitted by contact with the nasal secretions of infected dogs.

Canine Leptospirosis

This is a bacterial disease that impairs renal (kidney) function and may result in kidney failure. Clinical signs include vomiting, impaired vision, and convulsions. The disease is transmitted by contact with objects that have been contaminated with the urine of infected animals.

Recommended Cat Vaccinations

Recommended Feline Vaccinations

Date	FVR-CP*	Pneumonitis (Chlamydiosis)	Rabies	Feline Leukemia

*Feline Viral Rhinotracheitis, Claicivirus, Panleukopia (Feline Distemper)

Feline Diseases

Feline Panleukopenia

This is also known as feline infectious enteritis and feline distemper. This disease is caused by a resistant virus that may remain infectious for more than a year at room temperature on inanimate objects. It is transmitted through blood, urine, feces, and nasal secretions, and even by fleas from infected cats. The disease destroys many of the cat's white blood cells. The disease is fatal for 50% to 70% of the cats that have it. Cats with feline panleukopenia seem lethargic, vomit, have a high fever, and are dehydrated. Sickness may go on 3 to 4 days after the first signs are noticed and before death occurs.

Feline Viral Rhinotracheitis, Feline Calicivirus, and Feline Pneumonitis

These are diseases of the respiratory tract of cats. Infected animals are highly contagious to other cats and may show either acute or chronic respiratory signs.

Feline Leukemia Virus

This is usually a fatal disease affecting the cat's immune system. This increases susceptibility to other diseases as well as leukemia. Signs of feline leukemia virus include weight loss, recurring or chronic illness, lethargy, fever, diarrhea, unusual breathing patterns, and a yellow color around the mouth and the whites of the eyes.

Warning Signs

Checking your pet on a weekly basis is the key to early detection or prevention of health problems. If eyes, ears, teeth, mouth, nose, feet and skin seem in good shape, terrific! But be aware of other warning signs to your pet's ill health.

If he suddenly seems aloof, not himself or uninterested in spending time with the family, talk to your veterinarian. Other dramatic changes in behavior such as whining, hiding, or urinating in the house may be symptoms of a bigger problem. Early intervention can prevent more serious conditions, so don't delay your visit to the veterinarian.

Pet Pages

The following are warning signs of potential problems with pet's health. If you spot any of these warning signs, call your veterinarian.

Changes in Appetite or Weight	Abnormal increase or decrease in appetite or weight
	Pet seems excessively thirsty
Vomiting	Is especially a cause for concern if vomit has blood or bile in it
	Note: Cat Hair balls. One of the most common causes for kitty vomiting is hair balls. This may be prevented by brushing your cat more frequently. This will reduce the amount of hair that she may swallow during her grooming sessions. Another way to help your cat is to regularly put a little petroleum jelly or butter on her paw for her to lick off. Be sure to rub it in a bit or kitty will butter the room.
	Cats are curious rascals and often eats things they shouldn't like string or rubber bands. Usually, they throw up these foreign objects later. If you catch kitty in the act, do not pull things out of her mouth. This may do more damage than good by harming kitty's intestines. Instead, call your veterinarian for advice.
Changes in Teeth	Loss of teeth, tartar build-up, bad breath, pale or bleeding gums
Changes in Excretion	Diarrhea or constipation that lasts over 24 hours or contains blood or mucous
	Increased urination, "accidents," difficulty urinating and passing little or no urine, urine that contains blood or is cloudy

Preventative Health Care

Abnormal Discharge	From eyes, ears, or nose
Changes in Fur	Balding in spots or coat becoming ragged and dull
Skin Irritations	Dry, flaking, skin
	Patches of red or inflamed skin, sores or irritations
Coughing or Breathing	Coughing, sneezing, excessive panting, shortness of breath or difficulty breathing
Limping	Limping on any leg, reluctance to move, difficulty getting up or down
Scooting	Dragging bottom on floor
Scratching	Head shaking, excessive scratching, licking or biting one particular area
Lumps	Bumps, lumps, or growths on or under surface of skin
Behavior Changes	Sudden viciousness, lethargy, hiding, or a change in sleeping patterns or position

Spay and Neutering

Let's face it, cats and dogs just aren't ready for contraception. They forget to take their pills and think condoms are chew toys. So it's up to us humans to help control the epidemic pet overpopulation problem by having pets spayed or neutered.

Every year, over 12 million abandoned cats and dogs are destroyed. Sterilizing cats and dogs is the only responsible choice.

Spaying Females

Rather than incur the responsibility of caring for unplanned puppies or kittens and the difficult task of finding them good homes, have your female pet spayed. Spaying your cat or dog improves her general well-being, greatly reduces the risk of breast cancer, and eliminates uterine infections. No more yowling, crying, or mess while she's in heat. And there'll be no need to confine your female pet during her heat cycle. A spayed female is also less likely to roam or have male suitors spraying on your property.

Neutering Males

Neutering your male pet will eliminate sexual frustration, prostate problems, and may help curb other behavior problems like aggression, mounting, and spraying. Additionally, a neutered male is less likely to stray, decreasing his chances of getting lost, hurt, or killed.

Contact the Following Groups For information on low-cost spay and neutering services:

- Friends of Animals   800-321-7387
- SPAY/USA   800-248-SPAY

Preventative Health Care

- SNAP 619-525-3047
  Spay Neuter Action Project

Dental Care

Think about how much you enjoy dental visits and care. Okay, take it one step further and you'll understand how loathsome your pets find this process. Not only do pets and humans have a distaste for dental care in common, we also share a real need for this preventive care. Regular dental care, like tooth brushing, dental chews, and cleanings by a veterinarian can prevent tooth loss, gum inflammation, and pain.

Brushing Pet's Teeth

Pets will probably never like having their teeth brushed. If necessary, you may need to restrain your pet in a towel or pet handling bag. Be sensitive to the fact that this is a frightening experience.

Let your pet get used to you checking inside her mouth by gently lifting one lip at a time. After a few inspections, she'll become more comfortable and less resistant to this. Then, touch pet's teeth with your finger and gently massage the teeth. Begin with the outside of the teeth, then massage in back as well. Do this every day for a few days until she seems tolerant of the process. Now, you are ready to move on to a finger brush or a pet toothbrush. You have mastered the art of pet dental care when you begin using pet toothpaste. Do not use human toothpaste or baking soda.

Avoiding Plaque and Tartar

Brushing pet's teeth is a must for avoiding plaque and tartar, but other precautionary steps may be taken as well. Have your veterinarian regularly check teeth and schedule cleanings when necessary. Feed your pet hard, dry food and give her chew toys designed to remove plaque such as rawhide and nubby Nylabone® chews.

Warning Signs of Dental Problems

Despite our best efforts, sometimes our pets have dental problems anyway. Preventive care will minimize the occurrence, but be on the lookout for signs of trouble. The sooner you detect a problem, the sooner you can get your pet proper care.

As you inspect your pet's mouth, check for swollen gums or cheeks, accumulation of tartar, sores, or pale gums. If your pet seems unusually reluctant to open his mouth, it could be because of dental problems. When he finally opens his mouth, a case of bad breathe could be a trouble sign.

As you observe your pet in his daily activities, you may notice he seems reluctant to eat — or seems to be uncomfortable when he does. If he drools excessively or has blood in his saliva, it's time for a trip to the veterinarian for a dental check-up.

Parasites

Pets can be attacked by a variety of internal and external parasites. Once again, prevention is the key.

Internal Parasites: What are They & How to Get Rid of 'Em...

Hookworm - Named for their hook-shaped teeth, these worms attach themselves to pet's intestinal lining and feed on their blood. Nice, huh? Hookworm can be fatal to puppies and kittens; so, if your pet seems lethargic, has a loss of appetite, or excretes a black, tarry stool, don't delay taking your pet to the veterinarian. Bring a stool sample for the doctor to analyze as well.

Preventative Health Care

Roundworm - Virtually all pets are born with this common parasite or get it while nursing. Older pets can contract roundworm during normal contact with soil infected by tiny roundworm eggs. Symptoms of roundworm are diarrhea and vomiting, bloated stomach, and a rough coat. Take pet and stool samples to the veterinarian.

Tapeworm - These little critters sneak into your pet's body through his digestive track. A swallowed flea or infested animal, typically a rodent, can be a vehicle for worms. Symptoms are more subtle, but parts of the worm can be seen in an infected pet's stool. Take pet and a stool sample to the veterinarian.

For Dogs Only

Heartworm - Living in the heart of a dog, these parasites are the most life-threatening. They stress a dog's heart which restricts blood flow to the organs and may cause failure, possibly leading to death. Keeping in mind that heartworm is easy to prevent and difficult to cure, ask your veterinarian to test your dog for heartworm then prescribe a preventive medication. Because heartworm plugs the heart of a dog, it impairs proper circulation. Symptoms of heartworm may be weight loss, lethargy, and poor endurance. Other warning signs of heartworm include exercise intolerance, labored breathing, and coughing.

Whipworm - These little buggers obviously never heard the age-old real estate adage: location, location, location. They choose to make their home at the lower end of a pet's digestive tract. Yes, that's exactly where you think it is. Preventive vaccines are key because whipworm is difficult to detect and evict. Some clues that your dog has whipworm will be chronic bowel inflammation, diarrhea, weight loss, and dehydration.

Tips for Preventing Worm Infestation:

- Keep pet away from soil contaminated with animal feces. (Parasites can transmit their eggs to pets who sniff or come into contact with infected fecal matter.)
- Stop pet from eating wildlife.
- Groom regularly (keep flea-free).
- Keep bedding clean.
- Have veterinarian check for worms regularly.

External Parasites: Fleas, Ticks, & Mites

Fleas

The scratching, the itching, the stinging - it's driving you and your pet nuts! Fleas are more than just irritating pests, they're the enemy. It's time to declare WAR. Combatting fleas will be an ongoing effort on your part. Without a long-term strategy, fleas will return and bring their friends.

If yours is an outdoor pet or if visitors have flea problems, eliminating fleas all together is nearly impossible. At best, you may be able to control them.

How to Detect a Flea Problem

If your pet is scratching himself often, you may have a flea problem. Comb pet with a flea comb and see if you catch any. They are tiny, dark bugs about the size of a grain of sand. If you have fleas, they will leave "flea dirt," which looks like black specks in your pet's fur. Flea dirt is typically found on a pet's back, tail, groin, or hindquarters area. Flea dirt may also be found where the pet sleeps.

Fleas do not make a permanent home on your pet.

Preventative Health Care

Unlike internal parasites, they love to travel and spend a great deal of time off your pet's body. In fact, 95% of your flea problem will be in your house and yard so it's important to treat the environment as well as the pet. Eliminating fleas requires a three-step plan. You must treat your pet, home, and yard to be effective.

De-Flea Your Pet

Using flea or citrus shampoo, bathe pets weekly. Between baths, comb pets with a flea comb and use powders or sprays designed to eliminate fleas. Add garlic or vinegar to your pet's food. Think about it, if you were a flea, would you want to drink blood spiked with garlic or vinegar? You might also give your pet an aloe vera drink to relieve skin irritation. After fleas are gone, your pet may still itch from previously irritated skin. Ask your veterinarian about shampoos that will relieve skin irritations.

Talk with your veterinarian about safe new products on the market designed for flea control. Many of these new products are only available through your veterinarian.

De-Flea Your Home

Wash all of your pet's bedding, slipcovers, throw rugs, and coverings weekly. Vacuum and sweep twice weekly and dispose of vacuum bags immediately.

Treat your entire home with a flea control product. Make sure you apply flea treatment everywhere — behind appliances, under cushions, under furniture, and especially the places your pet likes to hang out. A cedar chip bed for your pet may repel fleas from the area.

De-Flea Your Yard

Remove food, water bowls, and toys from yard before treating area. Concentrate on treating moist areas and places where your pet spends a lot of time. Some flea treatment products can be dispersed using a sprayer connected to your water hose. Diatomaceous earth or pyrethrum dust are considered natural alternative treatments, or you can try nematodes — insects that attack and destroy flea larvae. These bugs are reportedly harmless to other bugs, birds, and animals.

Flea Maintenance

For a week or two after treating your yard, you may notice an increase in flea activity. Don't worry, this is normal. Flea pupae is impossible to kill and vacuuming or other activity may actually stimulate hatching. These young fleas will soon meet their demise by flea treatment residual left in your house, on your yard, and on your pet.

Congratulate yourself for a job well done, but remember that regular maintenance is essential to keeping fleas under control. Even when you don't see fleas, keep up the shampooing and treatments. Consult your veterinarian on flea control and ask which products she recommends. To avoid adverse reactions from incompatible products, consult your veterinarian before combining products.

Good luck! And for the sake of your family and pet's comfort, be persistent in your routine.

Ticks and Mites

Just when you thought it was safe to keep reading; just when you thought all discussion of creepy, crawly, wiggly parasites was over; just when you thought you'd heard it all, there's one more group of parasites to learn about: ticks and mites. However unsettling this is for you, it is important to fully understand what pets are up against. Your pet's best defense against disease and parasites is an educated owner;

so hang in there. The section on Frisbee™ tossing is coming soon.

Ticks

Pets typically pick up ticks during outdoor excursions. Check pet's skin regularly for ticks. A number of diseases are transmitted via tick bites.

Tick Removal

Use tweezers to remove the tick from your pet's body. Be sure to get the whole tick; leaving a part behind could cause sores and infection. Avoid directly handling the tick if possible by using tissue or latex gloves. Afterwards, wash hands thoroughly. Dab hydrogen peroxide or rubbing alcohol on the area to prevent infection. Tick removal tools are available.

Ear Mites

Ear mites look like dark, granular substance in your pet's ears. Don't dismiss it as dirt. Left untreated, ear mites can cause hearing loss. If pet shakes his head or scratches his ears with paws, talk to your veterinarian.

Pet Nutrition

Another thing pets and humans have in common is a need for a balanced diet. Proper nutrition is critical to your pet's health and well-being.

Premium Pet Food

Premium pet food is more expensive, yet at the same time more economical. Allow us to explain: Nutrients in premium food are more concentrated and are absorbed better by pets. Therefore, you use less food than you'd have to with a cheaper brand. Say you've got Primo Dog Chow which costs $10 and lasts your pooch two weeks; and Cheapo Brand Dog Food which costs $7, but only lasts five days. The more expensive food is actually the better deal. It tastes great, and is more filling. Does your pet deserve any less? And let's not forget the benefits to you: More absorption by pet equals less poop.

Nutrition Needs

Manufacturers offer foods that meet specific nutritional needs of pets in certain age or size classifications. For instance, you wouldn't want to feed your active, growing puppy the same food as you would Grandpa Lassie. Choose the food that meets your pet's age and activity level (Puppy, Kitten, Adult, Active, Inactive, Senior).

Feeding Tips

Each pet should have his own food dish, set at least three feet apart from the next closest pet bowl. If your pet is tall, elevate the bowl so he doesn't have to strain to reach it. Only use food supplements if your veterinarian recommends it.

People food is generally a bad idea for pets because it does not meet their nutritional needs and adds unnecessary calories to their diet. If you absolutely can't resist sharing your food with a begging pet, limit table scraps to no more than 10% of pet's diet. Put scraps in pet's bowl or a pet will become your shadow at the table. Pets who are rewarded for begging can become a nuisance, especially to guests who want to enjoy their meal without a guilt trip from Miss Kitty.

Never feed a pet chocolate or onions. Bones can also be dangerous for a pet. Before giving your pet any bones, please talk with your veterinarian first.

Select nutritious snacks for your pet that can be given as treats during training or between meals. Fresh fruit and vegetables like carrots, apples, and grapes make great snacks. Give your pets snacks sparingly and never use as a replacement for regular meals.

Feeding A Cat

There are basically three options for a cat's feeding schedule:

1) **Like Clockwork** - Feed cat at same time each day. After a set time, remove the food bowl and any leftovers.

2) **Measured Feeding** - Allow only a certain amount of food to be placed in a bowl which kitty has access to all day.

3) **Bottomless Bowl** - Fill cat bowl whenever it's empty. Just keep that food coming, regardless of time of day or amount she's already eaten. This feeding method is not a good idea for overweight cats.

Tip: To slow down an overzealous eater, put small, clean one-to-two-inch diameter rocks in food bowl. Your cat will have to slow down to pick the food out of the rocks.

Cat Grass: Some cats enjoy nibbling on grass and it's okay. You may want to grow grass specifically for your kitty; this may keep her out of your other houseplants. Don't use grass seeds that are dyed or have been chemically treated.

Don't: Feed your cat dog food. It doesn't contain the right balance of nutrients for a cat.

Do: Use caution when giving milk to adult cats; many are lactose intolerant and will get diarrhea.

Feeding a Dog

Schedule regular meal times for your dog which last about 30 minutes before you remove the food bowl. Always keep fresh water available for your pooch. If you change pet food, gradually mix old and new food. This gives your dog a chance to get used to the new food and minimize digestive upsets which may result in diarrhea. Once you find a brand both you and your dog are happy with, stick with it. Avoid feeding an hour before or after rigorous activity.

Obesity

Pets have no vanity. They're not going to check themselves out in the mirror, realize swim suit season is fast-approaching, and high-tail it over to gym. It's up to you to be your pet's weight watcher.

When you place your hands on your pet's rib cage, do you feel his ribs? Or do you dig through a sea of blubber to find them? Does his rib cage seem lost all together? Has your pet lost his waist? Does that "tuck up" seem tuckered out? If you answered "yes' to any of the last four questions, you've been overfeeding your pet. It's time to begin a weight-loss regiment.

Excess weight and obesity is not only uncomfortable for your pet, it's unhealthy. Obese pets may fatigue easily, lack energy, stress joints, and be less mobile. Overweight pets are also more prone to injury and increase stress on vital organs such as their heart, lungs, liver, and kidneys. If your pet should need surgery, excess weight will increase the health risks.

Trimming Down Your Chubby Buddy

Talk to your veterinarian about how to safely trim down an overweight pet. She can offer diet and exercise tips for your fat cat or round hound. She may suggest decreasing food portions or switching pet food to one that is low fat.

Exercise will be necessary. Talk with your veterinarian about your pet's health. She will have advice on what amount of exercise is reasonable for your pet. Begin slowly and gradually increase your pet's activity. As your pet establishes this new lifestyle, you will notice a renewed, happier, and more energetic pet emerging. Your pet will also enjoy the additional active time and attention he will receive from you as you participate in his exercise program.

If you want to feed your dog snacks, make sure that they are low fat snacks such as carrots, oranges, apples, seedless grapes, bananas, pretzels, and unbuttered popcorn.

Care and Handling Tips

Giving a Cat a Pill

Never give a pet human medication unless your veterinarian approves. It could be harmful to your pet. If you must give your cat a pill, you might try a specially designed pill plunger. Or you could hide the pill in pureed baby food or her favorite moist cat food. Make sure she actually eats the pill instead of maneuvering her way around it.

The following is the direct approach of depositing pills into a cat's mouth. It may sound complicated, but it's really not. Try acting it out with an imaginary cat as you read; you'll realize it's actually quite simple:

- Butter the pill to make it slippery;
- Sit on the floor, bend open legs with feet together, creating a diamond shaped border in which to place the cat;

- Back your cat's legs into your body;
- Gently open kitty's mouth by applying slight pressure on short teeth (right behind their "fangs");
- Drop pill as far back into the throat as possible;
- Close mouth, tip head gently up;
- Softly stroke throat from top to bottom to encourage swallowing;
- Mission accomplished when you feel the gulp of the swallowed pill.

Don't Let the Cat Outta the Bag

When giving cats pills, baths, or when grooming, you may find it helpful to wrap kitty in a towel to inhibit her movement and prevent scratching. You may also purchase a special cat handling bag for this purpose. Whether using a cat bag or towel, make sure all four legs and paws are secured and kitty's head is sticking out.

Giving a Dog a Pill

When giving your dog a pill, try hiding it in his food and sprinkling it with onion powder. As with cats, make sure your dog has eaten the pill, not just shuffled it around from one side of the bowl to the other. To insert a pill directly into your dog's mouth, lubricate it with a little butter first. Then tilt his head back, place pill on back of tongue, remove your fingers and close dog's mouth. Rub throat gently to induce swallowing. If veterinarian approves, reward your brave friend with a treat.

16 Grooming

Grooming is a necessary part of your pet's care so have fun with it! Your attitude and approach to grooming will set the tone. Having a good attitude, patience, and a smile will help put your pet at ease. Many pets enjoy grooming (at least the brushing part). This is their one-on-one time with you, where they get your undivided attention. So, relax, laugh, and praise your pet for his grooming tolerance.

Regular grooming keeps your cats and dogs feeling, looking, and smelling their best. It can also offer valuable insights into your pet's health and well-being. A grooming session should include brushing, checking ears, eyes, feet and teeth, bathing (if needed), hair clipping for some pets, and a delicious treat for being such a sport (that's for the pet, not you).

Benefits of Grooming

Regular grooming stimulates circulation and distributes oils, helping your pet maintain a beautiful coat and healthy skin. This routine handling can also alert pet parents to any possible parasite, skin, or medical problems early on.

The Grooming Process

Begin grooming immediately with short, enjoyable sessions. Slowly accustom pet to the grooming routine. Establish a routine and groom systematically so your pet knows what to expect. Start with their head and back, then gradually add their tail, legs, and their sensitive tummy. Keep the sessions short in the beginning and lavish pet with praise and a treat at the end of the session. Remember to keep it fun!

Begin With Brushing

Types of Brush

Brushing your pet's coat is a good place to start. But, before you can begin, you must have the right grooming tools. Tools are available for all types of fur. If you have a short hair pet, soft or medium bristle brushes work well. Rubber mitts also work well for removing dead hair and redistributing oils. For long coats, you will need a comb to gently work out tangles and follow with a long bristle brush. If your

Grooming

pet has a double coat, then a slicker brush or rake comb is needed. If you are unsure as to which grooming tools you need, ask your veterinarian or a groomer for their advice.

Tangles

Remove tangles with fingers or a wide-toothed comb. For your pet's comfort, avoid pulling or yanking on hair; it hurts. There are special combs available for those tough knots.

Brushing

When brushing, use short gentle strokes and work a small area at a time. Brush with — not against — the natural direction of hair. Remember, you're not styling or teasing puppy's hair for a night on the town.

Clean Eyes & Ears

Dampen a cotton ball, wash cloth, or tissue to wipe eyes. Gently wipe from inside corner to outside. Use new cloth on each eye to avoid spreading of possible contaminants. Use warm water to make this as comfortable for your pet as possible.

Wipe pet's ears with a warm, wet washcloth or cotton ball. Use a fresh wipe for each ear to avoid spreading germs. Don't use cotton swabs; they may push wax into the ear. If your pet has excessive ear wax, redness, or has an odor, contact your veternarian. This may be a symptom of a medical problem.

Paw Care

Neglected nails can be painful to pet and harmful to others. Additionally, overgrown nails can cause damage to home and clothing. Check nails weekly and trim as necessary. Don't forget about those dewclaws (the "thumb" that's a little higher than the other four).

Use this opportunity to inspect paws and pads for pebbles, foxtail grass, or any other foreign objects.

For new pet owners, you may want to ask your vet or groomer to demonstrate how to trim nails first. This is probably the least favorite grooming ritual for your pet because if you trim too short, it is painful.

The idea is to keep your pet's nails at a comfortable length. Too short or too long is not comfortable. Slowly trim each nail from top to bottom, rather than from side to side which can pinch. Be careful not to cut into the "quick" which hurts and will bleed. The quick looks like a shadow of the nail inside it. It may be red or have a pinkish color. It is living tissue and your pet will experience pain if it is cut. After trimming, be sure to file the nail to smooth rough edges and prevent injury to you, your pet, or your furnishings.

If you accidentally cut the quick, stop the bleeding with styptic powder, flour, or cornstarch. This may sting a bit.

Bathing

Cats typically do not need, and especially don't want, you to bathe them. They groom themselves and only need to be bathed if they have a flea or tick problem, special allergies, got into a messy situation (junior spilled his chocolate milk on miss kitty), or aren't properly grooming themselves.

Dogs usually aren't crazy about baths either. And, just like cats, they should only be bathed when they have flea or tick problems, skin allergies, or are just dirty. Keep in mind that bathing too frequently is not good for a dog. It robs his skin of essential oils and can leave him with dry, itchy, sensitive skin. And sometimes when your dog is a bit, shall we say, malodorous, it does not mean he needs a bath. Dogs with clean coats can smell bad because of dirty ears

Grooming

or teeth, or full anal glands. So, a bath wouldn't solve your smelly dog dilemma.

Preparing for Pet's Bath

- Accept the fact that you will be getting wet and dress accordingly.
- For pet's stability, place a rubber mat or towel in the sink or bathtub.
- Have your towels, pet shampoo, and tub ready.
- Use warm water at a comfortable temperature.
- Be sure pet can fit into sink or bathtub.
- Brush pet's coat and trim nails before bath.
- Put cotton balls in ears to prevent soap and water from getting in.

Bath Time

Begin washing your pet's head and face with a damp washcloth, carefully avoiding eyes and ears. For pets with fleas, before getting your pet wet, start by applying a ring of shampoo around your pet's neck. This will stop fleas from rushing to your pet's head for safety. Remember, this is an unnatural and scary experience for a pet. Use a soothing voice, reassure them that everything is okay. If your pet has a clean head and face and seems upset when this area is washed, you may consider skipping it and begin your shampooing at the neck.

Be sure you are using pet shampoo; the PH in human shampoo is too harsh for pets and can leave skin dry and flaky. A spray attachment can make rinsing much simpler. Whatever your method of rinsing your pet, be careful of spraying or pouring water in pet's face. First of all, they don't like it and secondly, you want to avoid getting shampoo in their eyes, nose, or mouth.

Work from head down to the neck, then move on to body and legs. Rinse well. Then rinse again. It is important to get all the shampoo out of pet's coat.

After the Bath

- Towel dry (most pets are so relieved to get out of the sink or tub that they seem to like the toweling off).
- You can try blow drying hair on a low setting. (If pet seems too upset, stop.)
- Keep dryer moving and at least six inches away from pet to avoid burning.
- Keep pet in a draft-free area until dry.
- Give a final brush to remove remaining loose hair.
- On cold weather days keep pet indoors until he's completely dry.
- If it is a warm day outside, you may consider bathing your pet by hose, in a tub or wading pool in the yard. When whether permits, air or towel drying will do, but if you want to keep your pet clean, do not let him loose in the yard while damp.

Clipping & Trimming

If She Don't Look Good, You Don't Look Good

While your dog need not sport the trendiest new hair cut, you'll want to trim and clip his coat for pet's comfort and protection. Talk to a groomer about hair cuts for your breed. Even if you sport a military buzz cut for yourself, don't trim your pet's hair too close to the skin. It won't give Private Fido any more discipline, and his hair serves the function of protecting him from exposure, insect bites, and skin injuries.

Professional Groomers

You may decide to take your pet to a professional groomer. There, she will get her nails trimmed, ears and eyes cleaned, brushed, bathed, and hair cut according to breed specifications.

Use the same care in selecting a groomer as you would in selecting a veterinarian.

Questions to Ask

- What are his credentials?
- Is he certified?
- How long has he been in business?
- Will your dog be in contact with other pets?
- What grooming products will be used?
- What drying techniques are used?
- Can you tour the facility to check cleanliness and see how other pets are treated?

Whether you chose to have a professional groom your pet or you do it yourself, the important thing is that your pet is groomed regularly. With the right attitude, patience, and a sense of humor you and your pet will enjoy the grooming process. And, most importantly, your pet will look and feel great.

17 Directory

Pet Pages

ANIMAL ADOPTIONS
See Page....129

ANIMAL WELFARE

Aarf 753-3091
Abandoned Animal Rescue Foundation

Animal Abuse Hotline 800-952-5400
Cal Tip (Fish & Game)

Animal Abuse Hotline 800-982-2873
Cruelty Complaints

Animal Abuse Hotline 800-989-abuse
Sd Humane Soc.

Animeals+A39 756-4117 ext232
Food For Pets Of Elderly

Bob Farners Wildlife Rescue 749-6737

Canine Blood Bank 299-7620
Dogs Donate Blood

Complaints Against Vets 466-3400
Vet Med Assoc.

Complaints Against Vets 714-523-0980
S Ca Vet Med Assoc.

Complaints Against Vets 916-920-7662
Board Of Examiners In Vet Med.

Emergency Animal Rescue 789-5775

Emergency Wildlife Rehab 443-3692
Injured/Orphaned 24 Hrs

Feral Cat Coalition 497-1599
Free Spay/Neuter/Release Wild Cats

Focas 685-3536
Friends Of County Animal Shelters

Foundation For The Care Of Indigent Animals
Dog & Cat Adoptions 466-9137

Friends Of Cats, Inc. 561-0361
Private Non-Profit Organization For Cats.

House Rabbit Soc. 490-9403

Howl 789-5033
Helping Our Wildlife

Last Chance For Animals 565-9508
Animal Rights Hotline

Living Free Animal Sanctuary 909-659-4684

Mercy Crusade 278-1745
Econ. Help For Spay/Neuter, Vet Bills

National Cat Protection Society 619-469-8771
Non-Profit Organization.
Adopt Out Cats. Tues - Sat 12-5.

Paws San Diego 234-PAWS
(Pets Are Wonderful Support)
Helping People With Aids Keep Their Pets

Performing Animal Welfare Soc. 209-745-2606
Dedicated To Saving Performing Animals
Through Sanctuary, Education, And Legislation.

Persian Cat Rescue 222-5907

Pet Assistance Foundation 697-PETS
Low Cost Spay/Neuter Info.

Poison Control Hotline 543-6000
Local Help For Poison Emergencies

Project Wildlife 225-9453

R-Pal 789-8736
Ramona Pet Awareness League

San Diego Animal Advocates 943-0330
Animal Rights Hotline

San Diego Humane Society & Spca
24 Hr. Hotline 1-800-98-ABUSE

Snap 525-3047
Spay/Neuter Action Project

Stop Taking Our Pets (S.T.O.P) 619-755-1700

United Animal Nations 1-800-440-EARS
Disaster Assist. & Preparedness Trning.

Wildlife Center
Eliminate Pound Seizures

ANIMAL SHELTERS
See Page....129

ANIMAL - VOLUNTEER PROGRAMS
See Page....73

Directory

APARTMENTS - PET FRIENDLY

ALPINE

Alpine Country Apartments — 445-8022
2660 Alpine Blvd.

Alpine Estates Apartments — 445-0771
1539 Tavern Rdl

Alpine Village — 445-4500
2055 Arnold Way

CARLSBAD

Camino Point Village — 434-6075
2260 Avenida Magnifica

Ocean Crest — 434-6101
2320 Via Clemente

Park La Costa — 943-1146
3393 Calle Canuna

Rising Glen — 434-0200
2300 Rising Glen Way

CASA DE ORO

Casa De Helix — 462-1212
3903 Conrad Dr.

CHULA VISTA

Moss Gardens — 420-4150
521 Moss St.

Woodlawn Gardens — 476-9933
535 Woodlawn Ave.

CLAIREMONT

Pacific Palms — 576-9372
5109 Clairemont Mesa Blvd.

COLLEGE AREA

Riviera De Ville — 279-6186
3235 Armstrong St.

DOWNTOWN

Cityfront Terrace — 696-6300
500 West Harbor Dr.

Greystone Lofts — 233-5638
541 Third Ave

Market St. Square — 696-0949
606 Third Ave

Seabridge — 696-6644
820 West G St.

Waverley Court — 235-9018
1075 19th St.

EL CAJON

Casa De Rosewood — 561-3353
12802 Mapleview St.

Amber Park — 593-7862
451 Ballantyne St.

Casa Bonita — 444-3898
1321 Greenfield Dr.

Evergreen Garden Apartments — 442-9935
291 Jamacha Rd.

Magnolia South — 447-2117
553 S. Magnolia

Oakdale Gardens — 447-8711
1343 Oakdale Ave.

Park West Apartments — 444-0224
376 W. Park Ave.

Parkside — 440-7654
304 North First St.

Portofino — 593-8707
822 South Mollison

Sandalwood Gardens — 440-7730
700 Ballantyne

Shady Lane — 444-4938
422 Shady Lane

Sunset View — 449-5153
1518 Sams Hill Rd.

The Grove — 442-7368
346 Jamacha Rd.

Timbers - El Cajon — 442-9847
1110 Petree St.

ENCINITAS

Torrey Pines Racquet Club — 942-7485
1720 El Camino Real

ESCONDIDO

Country Club Villas — 743-1699
2000 Montego Ave

Courtyard Gardens — 745-9314
508 East Mission Ave.

Creekside Village — 745-9911
2035 South Escondido Blvd.

El Norte Villas — 746-8661
1051 West El Norte Pkwy.

Greentree Townhomes — 743-0848
1433 N. Broadway

APARTMENTS - PET FRIENDLY (continued)

Oak Hill   738-9950
1302 Oak Hill Dr.

Qual Creek   741-1235
1815 N. Broadway

Summer Creek   489-8989
640 West Lincoln Ave

Villa Capri - North County   747-2444
910 E. Washington Ave.

Woodcreek Apartments   489-8161
830 West Lincoln Ave.

FALLBROOK
Pineview   728-0162
1101 Alturas Rd.

IMPERIAL BEACH
Royal Apartments   424-3314
915 E. 4th St.

LA JOLLA
La Jolla Village   457-3020
8460 Via Mallorca Dr.

LA MESA
Casa De Helix   462-1212
3903 Conrad Dr.

Casa La Mesa   462-7270
4395 70th St.

Conrad Villas   697-6323
3917 Conrad Dr.

La Mesita   562-5900
7350 La Mesita Place

Mellmanor Townhomes   689-0505
8685-A Mellmanor Dr.

Spring Gardens   464-4255
4201 Spring St.

Spring Hill   469-3207
4341 Spring St.

Spring Terrace   464-2471
4242 Spring St.

Villages Of La Mesa   463-1116
5636 Amaya Dr.

Woodbridge Mt. Helix   670-1402
10874 Calle Verde Dr.

LAKESIDE
Casa De Rosewood   561-3353
12802 Mapleview St.

Julian Estates   390-0426
9727 Channel Rd.

Lake Jennings Apartments   561-2650
12625 Mapleview

Laurel Park   561-7086
12760 Laurel St.

Maplewood Apartments   561-8732
12715 Mapleview

Marilla Sundance   561-2922
9660 Marillo Dr.

Stoneridge   443-0893
12840 Mapleview

Willow Creek Lakeside   561-8400
9413 Winter Garden Blvd.

Wintercrest Village   443-6702
12002 Wintercrest Dr.

Woodglen   390-9753
12905 Mapleview St.

LEMON GROVE
Hillside Terrace   698-2000
3262 College Place

MIRA MESA
Hourglass Park Apartments   271-4151
9505 Gold Coast Dr.

Maya Linda   566-5350
9646 Carroll Canyon Rd.

MISSION BAY
Bay View Summit   276-1133
3103 Clairemont Dr.

MISSION VALLEY
Mission Knolls   283-9515
4580 Zion Ave

NORTH PARK
North Park Properties   298-1630
3792 31st St.

OCEANSIDE
Island Club   758-0700
2300 Catalina Circle

Libby Lake Apartments   757-5643
506 Calle Montecito

Directory

APARTMENTS - PET FRIENDLY (continued)

Meadowbrook 612 Los Arbolitos	433-1614
Ocean Breeze 960 Vine St.	967-0999
Ocean View Terrace 440 Canyon Dr.	721-8807
Raintree 3699 Barnard Dr.	433-2224
Sea Bluffs 2500 Sea Cliff Way	433-2900
Shadow Way 4771 Yuma Ave.	940-0563
The Villages Of Monterey 3901 Mesa Dr.	967-6646
Villa Camino 2051 Geneva	433-0223
Village North 854 Vine St.	721-1921
Vista Del Oro 4401 Mission Ave.	722-5226
Vista Way Village 3522 Vista Way Village Dr.	967-7100

POINT LOMA

Loma Palisades 2799 Adrian St.	222-0461
Loma Portal 3131 Cauby St.	222-0011
Pacific Isle 3050 Rue D'Orleans	224-3316

POWAY

Silver Oak - Poway 13409 Midland Rd.	748-5570

RANCHO BERNARDO

Bernardo Crest 11820 Paseo Lucido	451-1283
Deerwood 15640 Bernardo Center Dr.	672-0707

RANCHO PENASQUITOS

Countryside 12556 Oak Knoll Rd.	748-4774

RANCHO SAN DIEGO

Calavo Woods 10850 Jamacha Blvd.	760-1858
Country Hills Tennis 2450 Hilton Head Place	442-7279
Lakeview Village 3115 Sweetwater Springs Blvd.	670-6400
Rancho Hillside 12367 Calle Albara	670-8171

SAN DIEGO

Baye Town Ii 625 13th St. #19	424-3292
Cabrillo Palisades 7901 Harmarsh	277-1060
Cabrillo Square 1399 Ninth Ave.	230-8200
Carmel Summit 11795 Stoney Peak Dr.	487-8102
Carmel Terrace 11540 Windcrest Ln.	451-0316
Emerald Palm Apartments 2271 Palm Ave	429-6130
Genesee Gardens Condo. Rentals 7911 Nightingale Way	278-2131
Harbor Ridge 3303 Clairemont Dr.	276-1188
Las Casitas 17115 West Bernardo Dr.	487-8007
Mission Trails 6975 Golfcrest Dr.	460-1500
Parklane 9669 Gold Coast Dr.	578-2332
Scripps Landing 9970 Erma Rd.	586-0206
Summit Park Village 8563 Lake Murray Blvd.	460-4673
Villa Del Sol 5474 Reservoir Dr.	680-4784
Villas At Camino Bernardo 11203 Paseo Montanoso	672-0057

SAN MARCOS

Barnham Villas 570 Barham Dr. E.	744-3334

APARTMENTS - PET FRIENDLY (continued)

Islands 715 Ash Lane	744-9339
Mission Park 221 Woodland Pkwy.	747-5700

SANTEE

Greystone Ridge 8777 Graves Ave.	562-9137
Mission Villas 9525 Mission Gorge Rd.	562-5900
Santee Villas 10445 Mast Blvd.	448-9330
Sunset Trails 8655 Graves Ave.	449-5030
The Oaks 9205 Carlton Oaks Dr.	448-7185
The Sycamores 9249 Carlton Oaks Dr.	448-5251

SERRA MESA

Gramercy Apartments 9072 Gramercy Dr.	565-9081

SPRING VALLEY

Canyon Park 1625 Canyon Rd.	464-3700
Casa Monterey 10108 Calle Marinero	670-0456
Casa Monterey 10108 Calle Marinero	670-0456
Kenwood Gardens 9209 Kenwood Dr.	698-1356
Spring Villas 8760 Jamacha Rd.	589-9966

TIERRASANTA

Eldorado Hills 3828 Pendiente Ct.	279-7368

VISTA

Breeze Hill 881 Soft Wind Rd.	945-1020
Casa Antiqua 1225 Palomar Place	724-9372
Copper Rose 560 Copper	726-3848
Emerald Pointe 333 North Emerald Dr.	726-7331
Foothill Courtyards 1360 Foothill Dr.	726-4854
Mesa Gardens 800 East Bobier Dr.	726-2532
Mesa Gardens 800 East Bobier Dr.	726-2532
Oak Manor 1575 Oak Dr.	724-0080
Oak Terrace 1440 Oak Dr.	758-4470
Shadowridge Country Club Apts 1617 Live Oak Rd.	727-0343
Shadowridge Glen 974-72 Lupine Hills Dr.	680-4738
Shadowridge Meadows 1515 South Melrose Dr.	680-4783
Shadowridge Park 2000 South Melrose Dr.	598-2705
Shadowridge Summerwind 1580 Shadowridge Dr.	598-0988
Shadowridge Woodbend 915 Brooktree Lane #115	727-0030
Silver De Vista 633 Ascot Dr.	726-2578
Sycamore 920 Sycamore Ave	598-2900
Taylor Brooke 911 Taylor St.	941-8896
Vista Hacienda 365-J Pomelo Dr.	945-1200

ASSOCIATIONS & GROUPS
See Page....63

BOARDING - KENNELS

BONITA

Bonita Boarding Kennel 5775 Quarry Rd	475-3850

Directory

BOARDING - KENNELS (continued)

Jensen's Kennel 479-7074
3655 Proctor Valley Rd

Sweetwater Valley Animal 479-4791
5540 San Miguel Rd

BONSALL

Rancho Del Rey 758-9247
6580 Camino Del Rey

Rancho Del Rey Kennels 724-0926
6572 Camino Del Rey

Vista Veterinary Hospital 724-7186
6009 W Lilac Rd

CARDIFF BY SEA

Sholyn Kennels 942-8668
Po Box 1077

CARLSBAD

Seacrest Kennels 438-2469
7250 Ponto Dr

CHULA VISTA

Chula Vista Veterinary Clinic 420-3984
80 Broadway

DEL MAR

Day Care For Dogs 436-1233
5730 Carmel Valley Rd.
See our coupon

EL CAJON

Birdwood Kennels 447-8020
1329 E Chase Ave

Blossom Valley Groom/Boarding
9400 Blossom Valley Rd 443-4271
See our coupon

Canine Center 441-9995
535 Floyd Smith Dr

Club Summerwinds Animal Resort 445-4800
5690 Dehesa Rd

El Cajon Valley Veterinary 444-9491
560 N Johnson Ave

Paul's Chihuahuas 443-6490
14173 Olde Highway 80

Temple Dell Kennels 445-2845
6032 Dehesa Rd

ENCINITAS

Alcala Pet Care 436-6619
1273 Crest Dr

Amy's Pet Care 942-0714
659 Camino El Dorado

Animal Keeper 753-9366
155 Saxony Rd
See our coupon

Encinitas Veterinary Clinic 753-1162
222 N Highway 101

Holiday Pet Hotel 753-6754
551 Union St

Pauline B Hughes Pomeranians 753-5807
1726 Crest Dr

ESCONDIDO

Animal Care Ctr Of Escondido 747-4100
1328 Mission Rd

FALLBROOK

Fallbrook Animal Lodge 728-0892
1115 E Mission Rd

Tiggeroo Kennels 723-3419
215 W. Fallbrook St.
See our coupon

LA JOLLA

Creature Comfort 581-1131
5555 Coral Reef Ave

La Jolla Pet Sitting 581-2076
7514 Girard Ave

La Jolla Veterinary Hospital 454-6155
7520 Fay Ave

LA MESA

Club Parkway Pet Resort 463-5492
8200 Parkway Dr

Fuerte Animal Hospital 440-1432
4620 Avocado Blvd
See our coupon

Great Danes 465-9507
9490 Loren Dr

La Mesa Pet Hotel 466-6166
8126 Center Dr

Lake Murray Village Veterinary 464-3177
5644 Lake Murray Blvd

BOARDING - KENNELS (continued)

Parkway Pet Hospital   463-9151
8200 Parkway Dr

LAKESIDE

Carter Kennels   561-1464
8755 Winter Gardens Blvd

Greywood Kennels   443-7605
9078 Winter Gardens Blvd

Kennedy's Kennels   443-8687
8934 Creekford Dr

Rasenhof German Shepherds   443-4694
11315 Pinehurst Dr

LEMON GROVE

Canine Lodge & Cattery   463-0719
8336 Broadway

San Diego Pet Hospital   462-6600
7368 Broadway # A

NATIONAL CITY

A Dog's World   267-2577
2869 Ridgeway Dr

Los Reyes Chihuahuas   475-8046
3021 Shelby Dr

OCEANSIDE

Animal Keeper   941-3221
3532 College Blvd
See our coupon

Mission Animal & Bird Hospital   433-3763
3308 Mission Ave

Oceanside Pet Hotel   757-2345
2909 San Luis Rey Rd

Temple Heights Animal Hospital   630-3590
4750 Oceanside Blvd # A2

POWAY

Animal Keeper   748-9676
12280 Oak Knoll Rd
See our coupon

Royal Serchek Samoyed Kennel   748-3191
14950 Garden Rd

RAMONA

Animal Artistry   789-7406
124 10th St

Kritter Kamp   788-6799
25155 Creek Hollow Dr

RANCHO SANTA FE

Club Pet Boarding   450-3627
6525 Calle Del Nido

Critter Sitters   756-9635
Po Box 8144

SAN DIEGO

Animals Of San Diego   295-1008
246 W Washington St

Best Friends Pet Care   565-8455
8020 Ronson Rd

Canine Image   279-3336
3520 Ashford St # D

Center Veterinary Clinic   271-1152
8977 Mira Mesa Blvd

Clairemont Village Pet Clinic   275-5752
3007 Clairemont Dr # G

Fon-Jon Boarding & Training   273-2266
5050 Santa Fe St

Mission Valley Kennels   282-0022
4325 Twain Ave

Morena Pet Hospital & Bird Ctr   275-0888
1540 Morena Blvd

Rose Canyon Animal Hospital   273-4680
4295 Jutland Dr

SAN MARCOS

Abc Veterinary Clinic   471-4950
330 Rancheros Dr # A

Falconmoor Animal Inn   745-2759
1049 E Mission Rd

Levitt Animal Hospital   744-5242
1155 Grand Ave

Palomar Animal Hospital   727-7622
2615 S Santa Fe Ave

San Marcos Training & Boarding   744-5171
130 S Twin Oaks Valley Rd

SANTEE

Rose Hill Kennels   448-9071
8756 Cottonwood Ave

SANTEE

Su-Ets Kennels   448-8760
10631 Prospect Ave

BOARDING - KENNELS (continued)

SOLANA BEACH
Rancho-Solana Pet Spa   755-9318
247 S Highway 101

SPRING VALLEY
Jay Bee's Kennels   463-0207
9124 Olive Dr

Spartan Kennels   461-5577
3971 Spring Dr

Spring Creek Kennel & Cattery
9279 Campo Rd.   463-1722
See our coupon

VALLEY CENTER
Alibi Acres   749-4100
16750 Paradise Mountain Rd

VISTA
Ce Ce Belle Pet Hotel   758-7322
29920 Margale Ln

Chez-Doral Poodles   758-2776
1408 Little Gopher Canyon Rd

Elenbusch Dog Boarding   726-2068
814 Crest View Rd

Et Al Building & Design   630-5800
1611 S Melrose Dr # A215

Tri-City Vet Clinic & Boarding   758-2091
1929 W Vista Way # J

Vista Veterinary Hospital   726-1234
1139 S Santa Fe Ave

BOARDING - PET SITTERS

BONSALL
Hometenders   728-5000
32313 Mountain View Rd

CARLSBAD
Jennifer's Home Pet Care   434-1516
Po Box 4178

DEL MAR
Menagerie Minders In Home Pet   481-2253
Po Box 2528

EL CAJON
Caring Critter Companions   579-3888
432 N Westwind Dr

Creature Comfort In-Your-Home   444-6265
305 W Palm Ave

House Sitters Intl   469-5700
2913 Freeborn Way

ENCINITAS
A Pampered Pet   436-7387
555 2nd St

Claudia's Tlc   632-0961
162 Coop Ct

Wagtime Pet Sitting   943-8761

ESCONDIDO
Happy Pets In-Home Svc   739-9661
140 E El Norte Pky # 71

LA JOLLA
Creature Comfort   581-1131
5555 Coral Reef Ave

Good Buddies Home Pet Care   453-6857

La Jolla Pet Sitting   581-2076
7514 Girard Ave

LA MESA
La Mesa Pet Sitting   698-7297
6062 Lake Murray Blvd

POWAY
Good Dog Training School   748-7943
12843 Papago Dr

RANCHO SANTA FE
All Creatures Pet Sitting Svc   756-2702
17625 Los Morros

Critter Sitters   756-9635
Po Box 8144

SAN DIEGO
Catie Green's All Critter Care   279-3457
3772 Mount Aladin Ave

Cory's Pet Sitting   487-0993
11550 Duenda Rd

For Pet's Sake   **284-5656**
PO Box 3421
See our coupon

House Sitters Intl   451-1617
16776 Bernardo Center Dr

BOARDING - PET SITTERS (continued)

Noah's Ark Pet Sitters   273-2660
5255 Mount Ararat Dr

Pet-Tenders   298-3033
Po Box 23622

Pet Valet   538-8577
Po Box 721782

Pet's Best Friend Pet Sitting   565-9317
5411 Via Carancho

Pet Sitters Assoc. Of San Diego County   1-800-4-Pet-Sit
See our coupon

Point Loma Pet Sitter   226-7387
2828 Upshur St

Professional Pet Grooming   483-4680
1843 Garnet Ave

SAN MARCOS
Pet & Plant Sitters   744-2115
Po Box 1915

Pet Tenders   727-6816
Po Box 1614

SANTEE
Quality Pet Care   449-2273
Po Box 712172

SOLANA BEACH
Perfect Pet   755-3308
201 S Highway 101

VISTA
Et Al Building & Design   630-5800
1611 S Melrose Dr # A315

CARPET CLEANING
ALPINE
Astro Carpet Svc   447-1150
344 Bridle Run Ln

CARDIFF BY SEA
Green Clean   632-1054
1760 Lake Dr

Servicemaster   436-7225
1252 Rubenstein Ave

CARLSBAD
Duraclean   729-2427
4315 Highland Dr

Jeff's Carpet Cleaning   729-0685
4330 La Portalada Dr

Steam King Carpet Cleaners   729-7777
1290 Las Flores Dr

CHULA VISTA
Air-O-Mist Cleaners   422-1453
280 Trousdale Dr # D

America's Finest Cleaning Co   262-5317
3712 Main St # 240

ASAP Chem-Dry   474-8914
670 Colorado Ave

Brian's Chem-Dry   285-9877
1430 3rd Ave

Dimension Chem-Dry   426-3416
1224 Tobias Dr

Fuss-Budget Carpet Cleaning   427-3556
1109 Cuyamaca Ave

In Home Carpet & Upholstery   420-5370
546 2nd Ave

Victor's Carpet Care   426-9119
422 Smoky Cir

CORONADO
Coronado Carpet Cleaning   437-4979
170 1/2 C Ave

EL CAJON
America's Dry Carpet Cleaning   579-1055
1264 Naranca Ave

Clean & Dry Carpet Cleaners   445-1405
115 Harbison Canyon Rd

Excel Carpet Svc   447-0294
492 Dewane Dr

Gold Star Carpet Cleaning   447-8803
1265 Avocado Ave

Magic Bubbles By Chem Dry   281-6583
938 S Mollison Ave

Western Carpet Svc   444-1670
2043 Hidden Crest Dr

ENCINITAS
Action Specialists   942-9702
211 N El Camino Real

CARPET CLEANING
(continued)

Bob's Carpet & Upholstery Clng 336 Sanford St	753-8750
Daniel's Carpet & Upholstery 1780 S El Camino Real	633-3100
Holiday Carpet Cleaners 1709 Caliban Dr	633-1463
One Day Carpet & Upholstery 711 Appleridge Dr	753-7651

ESCONDIDO

All Clean Chem-Dry 759 Linwood St	489-7618
Amwest House & Carpet Cleaning 731 W 4th Ave # B	739-1442
Chem-Dry 2343 E Mission Ave	741-9110
Clean-All 1622 Birch Ave	740-9322
Correct Carpets & Draperies 2848 Oak Hill Dr	741-4047
Empire Steam Clean 1259 Summit Pl	487-3759
Hoover Dry Cleaners 140 W 2nd Ave	745-6821
Martin's Carpet & Upholstery 505 San Pasqual Valley Rd	745-0310

LAKESIDE

Carpet Repairman 13535 Brett Harte Dr	561-8396
Jack's Carpet & Upholstery 10880 Highway 67	561-2472

LEMON GROVE

Servicemaster 6975 North Ave # B	287-7070

NATIONAL CITY

Chem-Dry 340 W 26th St # C	286-7800
Cleanway Carpet Cleaners 2923 Alta Dr	262-6818

OCEANSIDE

A Emergency Carpet Svc 258 Rancho Del Oro Dr	722-6308
Allan Chem-Dry 105 Copperwood Way # C	741-4074
Amwest House & Carpet Cleaning 1818 Peacock Blvd	940-2088
Chem-Dry 244 Riverview Way	721-1135
Chem-Dry 5420 Blackberry Way	941-4441
Doctor Chem-Dry 836 Pillar Point Way	940-1033
Duraclean Carpet & Upholstery 178 N Barnwell St	757-5038
Monarch Chem-Dry 836 Pillar Point Way	(714) 661-1103
Servpro 2803 Cottingham St	967-0919
Servpro 4100 Avenida De La Plata	941-4300
State Of The Art Carpet 2365 Carriage Cir	722-5383

POWAY

Dirt Busters 13412 Pomerado Rd	486-3478
Real Mc Coy Carpet Cleaner 13710 Silver Lake Dr	748-5725
Servpro 12900 Brookprinter Pl	748-7378

RAMONA

San Vicente Carpet & Uphlstry 1138 D St	789-5099

SAN DIEGO

A Star Carpet Co 4286 34th St	282-4000
Alex Carpet Cleaning Co 4597 Lyric Ln	565-7237
Bob's Chem-Dry Carpet Cleaning 9285 Chesapeake Dr # B	535-0151
Carpet Brigade 4555 1/2 Thorn St	280-3747
Carpet Masters Of San Diego 4552 Lyric Ln	560-1660
Chem-Dry 10889 Caravelle Pl	448-0863

CARPET CLEANING
(continued)

Chem-Dry 8666 Lake Murray Blvd # 261	297-3188
Chem-Dry 8034 Hillandale Dr	589-5566
Chem-Dry 10464 Clairemont Mesa Blvd	298-2101
Chem-Dry 340 26th St # C	475-4459
Chem-Dry 5694 Mission Center Rd	281-6583
Chem-Dry 7960 Silverton Ave	487-1077
Chem-Dry 9285 Chesapeake Dr # B	565-6404
Chem Dry R-Gee Carpet Cleaning 4715 Oporto Ct	277-4245
Clean Team 7167 Hyatt St	454-7446
Del's Carpet & Upholstery Clng 4689 Huggins St	459-9390
Great American Chem-Dry 7960 Silverton Ave	281-2255
Hamilton Carpet Cleaning *See our coupon*	**738-9461**
J Klatt Carpet & Upholstery 4367 Conner Ct	270-1881
Kenn's Jet Steam 8305 Vickers St # 108	490-0370
Magic Touch 3350 Market St	234-6602
Mc Call's Carpet Cleaning 7904 Hillandale Dr	583-6411
Mission Carpet Cleaning *See our coupon*	**259-0557**
Sea Breeze Chem-Dry 3638 Camino Del Rio N	282-3324
Servpro 9915 Businesspark Ave	277-5494
Servpro 10961 San Diego Mission Rd	280-2377
Servpro Of Scripps-Mesa 8695 Hydra Ln	271-1519
Stanley Steemer Carpet Cleaner 9770 Candida St	271-9910

SAN MARCOS

Clean Master Carpet Cleaners 1165 Linda Vista Dr # 106	753-4339
Quick Dry Flood Svc 293 Venture St	235-8111
Steamworks 837 Grand Ave	471-7141

SANTEE

Exceptional Carpet Svc 9717 Pebble Beach Dr	448-8575
Flood Busters 9840 Prospect Ave	236-0270
Thompson's Carpets 9962 Prospect Ave # A	448-8888

SPRING VALLEY

La Mesa Carpet Cleaners 9860 Dale Ave # D7	463-2720
Morning Star Chem-Dry Carpet 3027 Avenida De Lamar	571-1600

VALLEY CENTER

A-1 Valley Ctr Carpet & Cleaning 28532 Canyon Rd *See our coupon*	**749-6469**

VISTA

Acme Janitoral Svc 405 Postal Way	729-1641
Affordable Carpet Care 1611 S Melrose Dr # A170	940-0593
Rancho Carpet & Window Clnng 568 Mason Rd	758-0074
Rex Carpet Cleaning Svc 2104 Riviera Dr	726-3093
Tag Cleaning Svc 557 Seaview Pl	945-4989

Directory

CAT SERVICES & PRODUCT SPECIALITIES

BONITA
Sweetwater Valley Animal — 479-4791
5540 San Miguel Rd

CARLSBAD
Golden Cat — 729-9343
Po Box 1759

EL CAJON
Friends Of Cats Inc — 561-0361
15587 Olde Highway 80

ENCINITAS
Alcala Pet Care — 436-6619
1273 Crest Dr

Animal Keeper — 753-9366
155 Saxony Rd

Cats Pajamas — 753-6754
551 Union St

ESCONDIDO
Animal Care Ctr Of Escondido — 747-4100
1328 Mission Rd

FALLBROOK
Grooming By Tiffany — 631-2671
1672 S Mission Rd # E

LAKESIDE
Carter Kennels — 561-1464
8755 Winter Gardens Blvd

NATIONAL CITY
Pet Plaza — 477-4076
911 E Plaza Blvd

OCEANSIDE
Mission Animal & Bird Hospital — 433-3763
3308 Mission Ave

Oceanside Pet Hotel — 757-2345
2909 San Luis Rey Rd

POWAY
Animal Keeper — 748-9676
12280 Oak Knoll Rd

SAN DIEGO
All Care Cat Hospital — 274-2287
4680 Clairemont Mesa Blvd

Best Friends Pet Care — 565-8455
8020 Ronson Rd

Best Of Breed Grooming — 299-9244
4503 Alabama St

Canine Coiffures — 459-2888
5155 La Jolla Blvd

Center Veterinary Clinic — 271-1152
8977 Mira Mesa Blvd

Cheshire Cat Clinic — 483-1573
1945 Garnet Ave # B

Exotic Pooch — 274-8660
969 Hornblend St

Pet-Tenders — 298-3033
Po Box 23622

Pet Kingdom — 224-2841
3191 Sports Arena Blvd

Poopsie Cat Products — 226-0655
3477 Channel Way

San Diego Humane Society — 299-7012
887 Sherman St

Satin Scissors — 224-2223
4314 Voltaire St

Shear Delite — 297-3470
818 Fort Stockton Dr

Squeak's Catique — 528-1010
4560 Alvarado Canyon Rd

Whiskers-The Ultimate Cat Shop — 234-6300
849 W Harbor Dr

SAN MARCOS
Falconmoor Animal Inn — 745-2759
1049 E Mission Rd

SANTEE
Exagere — 562-6303
8733 N Magnolia Ave # 125

EMERGENCIES - PET CARE & HOSPITALS
See Page....101

EMERGENCIES - PET LOST & FOUND
See page...111

GROOMING

ALPINE

Alpine Creek Pets   445-6868
1347 Tavern Rd # 16

Alpine Grooming   445-2006
1730 Alpine Blvd

Love On A Leash   445-4802
2241 W Victoria Dr

BONITA

Bonita Boarding Kennel   475-3850
5775 Quarry Rd

Margaret's Dog Grooming   475-5702
4244 Bonita Rd # A

BORREGO SPRINGS

Loving Care Pet Grooming   767-3321
860 Palm Canyon Dr

CARDIFF BY SEA

Carm's In Cardiff   436-4573
112 Aberdeen Dr

Sholyn Kennels   942-8668
Po Box 1077

CARLSBAD

Bark Shoppe   729-1708
592 Carlsbad Village Dr

Fortune's Grooming Salon   436-2442
7750 El Camino Real

Karen's Custom Grooming   431-7553
7130 Avenida Encinas # 100

Lucky Pup   729-3198
2786 State St

CHULA VISTA

Alfredo's Dog Grooming   425-2341
1152 3rd Ave

Dog Gallery   472-1777
1172 3rd Ave # D8

Gina's Pretty Pet Grooming   427-4027
1040 3rd Ave

Petland Inc   482-7712
585 Telegraph Canyon Rd

Tails-A-Wag'n   420-0169
1177 3rd Ave

CORONADO

Cylynda's Pedigree Svc   435-3635
1011 Orange Ave

Pollyanna Grooming Parlour   435-4934
1108 10th St

Urban Animals   239-2242
518 3rd St

DEL MAR

Currycomb   755-2677
1210 Camino Del Mar

Wag-N-Wheels   496-3362
N. Coastal, Rancho Sante Fe, La Jolla areas. *See our coupon*

EL CAJON

Alpine Grooming   390-0202
13794 Highway 8 Business

Angel's Pet Parlor   444-9490
2441 Jamacha Rd

Animal House Grooming Shop   442-7387
1286 Greenfield Dr

Barbara's Grooming   579-1830
1137 N 2nd St

Beth's Pet Spa   588-2726
1028 Broadway

Birdwood Kennels   447-8020
1329 E Chase Ave

Blossom Valley Groom/Boarding
9400 Blossom Valley Rd   443-4271
See our coupon

Broadway Animal Hospital   444-1166
380 Broadway

Canine Center   441-9995
535 Floyd Smith Dr

Catac Customized Animal   447-7366
1325 E Main St

Dorinda's Pretty Pup   447-7366
1325 East Main
See our coupon

El Cajon Pet   444-2303
1255 E Main St # A

French Cut   444-2942
685 Jamacha Rd

Pet Supply Warehouse   441-5200
540 N 2nd St

GROOMING (continued)

Rancho San Diego Animal Hospital 660-6767
2990 Jamacha Rd # 176

Teddy's Dog House 579-7811
1215 N 2nd St

Tender Loving Care Dog Grooming 447-6585
1428 Broadway

Vets Pets 469-3474
522 E Chase Ave

ENCINITAS

A Pampered Pet 436-7387
555 2nd St

Alcala Pet Care 436-6619
1273 Crest Dr

Animal Keeper 753-9366
155 Saxony Rd

Cats Pajamas 753-6754
551 Union St

Dog In Suds 943-0653
366 N El Camino Real

Loving Care Pet Grooming 436-1635
555 2nd St

Paws & Claws 634-1200
1403 Encinitas Blvd # D

Puppy Love Pet Grooming 634-1559
191 N El Camino Real

ESCONDIDO

4 Feet & Feathers Pet Store 480-0858
1835 S Centre City Pky # G

A Master's Touch 740-9274
555 W Country Club Ln

Cathy's Canine Salon & Btq 745-1700
2205 E Valley Pky

Cold Nose Grooming Salon 741-2707
254 W 8th Ave

Critter Corner 746-5422
316 W Mission Ave # 117

El Norte Pets 747-8337
322 W El Norte Pky

FALLBROOK

Country Grooming 723-2707
112 W Beech St

Fallbrook Animal Lodge 728-0892
1115 E Mission Rd

Fallbrook Grooming 728-8733
1672 S Mission Rd

Grooming By Tiffany 631-2671
1672 S Mission Rd # E

Lovin' Friends Grooming 728-8647
1221 S Mission Rd

Pampered Pets 723-2332
1672 S Mission Rd

IMPERIAL BEACH

Priced Rite Pets 575-8881
775 Palm Ave

South Bay Pet Supply & Groom 424-9942
753 Emory St

LA JOLLA

AAA Pet Professionals 456-1552
6905 La Jolla Blvd

Classic Grooming Of La Jolla 459-0302
7760 Fay Ave

Snooty's Classic Grooming 454-8020
1110 Torrey Pines Rd

Village Pet Shop 454-5449
5622 La Jolla Blvd

LA MESA

Andy's Pet Salon 698-4933
7750 University Ave

Bark Avenue Pet Salon 670-9422
3657 Avocado Blvd

Doggie Depot 697-8565
6165 Lake Murray Blvd

La Mesa Pet Hotel 466-6166
8126 Center Dr

Lake Murray Grooming 462-7297
6062 Lake Murray Blvd

Niki's Neat & Trim Pet Groom 589-1106
8681 La Mesa Blvd

LAKESIDE

Carter Kennels 561-1464
8755 Winter Gardens Blvd

Greywood Kennels 443-7605
9078 Winter Gardens Blvd

Varsity Kennels 561-3037
8447 Winter Gardens Blvd

GROOMING (continued)

LEMON GROVE

Canine Lodge & Cattery 8336 Broadway	463-0719
Lemon Grove Pets 7116 Broadway	460-1963
M & M's Family Pet Grooming 7249 Broadway	466-5215
San Diego Pet Hospital 7368 Broadway # A	462-6600

NATIONAL CITY

A Dog's World 2869 Ridgeway Dr	267-2577
Fiesta Pet Shop 1145 Highland Ave # A	477-5997
Pet Plaza 911 E Plaza Blvd	477-4076

OCEANSIDE

Animal Keeper 3532 College Blvd	941-3221
Groomingdales 2805 Oceanside Blvd	757-6477
Mission Animal & Bird Hospital 3308 Mission Ave	433-3763
Oceana Pet Stop 563 Vista Bella	439-6060
Oceanside Pet Hotel 2909 San Luis Rey Rd	757-2345
Square One Enterprises 1748 Maxson St	967-8648
Tails A Waggin 625 S Hill St	722-0811
Temple Heights Animal Hospital 4750 Oceanside Blvd # A2	630-3590

POWAY

Animal Keeper 12280 Oak Knoll Rd	748-9676
Beauty & The Beast 14025 Poway Rd # 1	679-9559
Dapper Doggery 12855 Pomerado Rd # D	748-7554
Fur Tailor 16336 Orchard Bend Rd	484-8105
Pet Supply Warehouse 13375 Poway Rd	679-2020
Poway Animal Hospital 12219 Poway Rd	748-3326
Poway Pets 14867 Pomerado Rd	748-2424

RAMONA

A Country Clip 2537 Main St	788-3722
Animal Artistry 124 10th St	789-7436
For Pet Sake Dog Grooming 19866 Highway 78	789-4023
Kathy's Country Pet Shop 1453 Main St	789-6272

RANCHO SANTA FE

Animals First 6525 Calle Del Nido	756-5545

SAN DIEGO

A Pom Pom 501 Cochran Ave	429-8543
All About Grooming 7525 Mission Gorge Rd	583-3644
Animal Antics Pet Grooming 6690 Mission Gorge Rd	284-7387
Animal Attraction 3368 Governor Dr	587-1677
Animals Of San Diego 246 W Washington St	295-1008
Arena Animal Hospital 3550 Rosecrans St # C	223-2166
Beauty & The Beast 9870 Hibert St # D9	679-9559
Berry Clean Dog Wash 4940 El Cajon Blvd	229-1232
Best Of Breed Grooming 4503 Alabama St	299-9244
Best Yet-Pet Spa 3117 1/2 54th St	286-0942
Better Grooming 4804 Gallatin Way	272-4301
Boulevard Animal Clinic 7047 El Cajon Blvd	582-7350

Directory

GROOMING (continued)

Cabrillo Veterinary Hospital 4138 Voltaire St	225-9684
Canine Castle 9353 Clairemont Mesa Blvd	571-1225
Canine Coiffures 5155 La Jolla Blvd	459-2888
Canine Image 3520 Ashford St # D	279-3336
Casa De Pets 10615 Tierrasanta Blvd # D	292-7387
Center Veterinary Clinic 8977 Mira Mesa Blvd	271-1152
Christine's Pet Grooming 4239 Park Blvd	299-6410
Clairemont Village Pet Clinic 3007 Clairemont Dr # G	275-5752
Critter Cleaners 9870 Hibert St	566-7890
Dapper Dog By Tiara 955 1/2 Turquoise St	488-9500
Dog Beach Dog Wash 4933 Voltaire St # C	523-1700
Exotic Pooch 969 Hornblend St	274-8660
Hair Of The Dog 4783 Narragansett Ave	223-3080
Hydro Surge Inc 7919 Silverton Ave # 412	560-1429
Kim's Kritters 11655 Duenda Rd	451-1815
Mc Kee Grooming & Training 7729 Othello Ave	560-7636
Menagerie 3511 5th Ave	295-4253
Mission Valley Kennels 4325 Twain Ave	282-0022
Mutt Hutt 3256 Greyling Dr	576-9714
My Beautiful Dog-O-Mat 3789 Park Blvd	295-6140
Newport Grooming 4892 Newport Ave	223-0662
Pacific Beach Pet Salon 1964 Garnet Ave	274-8844
Palm Ridge Grooming Gallery 4370 Palm Ave # T	690-1010
Paw Alley 2535 1/2 Clairemont Dr	276-3093
Penasquitos Pets 13223 Black Mountain Rd	484-3809
Pet Deco 8736 Lake Murray Blvd	466-9681
Pet Haven 4611 Seda Dr	560-7646
Pet Metro 3994 Clairemont Mesa Blvd # A	483-4100
Pet Pawlor 12540 Oaks North Dr	673-1777
Pet Supply Warehouse 1210 W Morena Blvd	275-5100
Petland Grooming 5430 Clairemont Mesa Blvd # D	268-3721
Petmart Discount Pet Supplies 6363 El Cajon Blvd	286-3474
Pink Poodle 4651 College Ave	583-2261
Point Loma 4870 Santa Monica Ave # 1a	222-4486
Point Loma Dog Wash & Grooming 2158 Catalina Blvd	222-4486
Poochies Self Svc Pet Wash Bar 6030 Santo Rd	541-2663
Preferred By Pets 3903 Voltaire St	223-9023
Professional Pet Grooming 1843 Garnet Ave	483-4680
Satin Scissors 4314 Voltaire St	224-2223
Shear Delite 818 Fort Stockton Dr	297-3470
Shelter Island Vet Clinic 1270 Scott St	222-0597

Pet Pages

GROOMING (continued)

Susie's Pet Clipet 3772 30th St	260-1030
Teddy's Dog House 5589 Clairemont Mesa Blvd	292-8676
Teddy's Dog House 6779 El Cajon Blvd	466-3194
Vip Grooming 9474 Black Mountain Rd # l	549-8800
Winston Sharpening 5958 Linnet St	266-0305

SAN MARCOS

Falconmoor Animal Inn 1049 E Mission Rd	745-2759
Felicia's Pet Grooming 135 S Rancho Santa Fe Rd	591-3919
Grooming by Beth **Hwy 78 & Nordahl** *See our coupon*	**432-0877**
Pet City Inc 1300 E Mission Rd	480-7301
Pet Supply Warehouse 1609 Capalina Rd	752-1300
Petite Pet Parlour 1241 W San Marcos Blvd	744-1335
Ye Olde Poodle Parlour 740 Nordahl Rd	745-9471

SANTEE

Bostone's Doggy Shop 8781 Cuyamaca St # M	449-6400
Jaws 'N Paws 9844 N Magnolia Ave	449-5301
Lakeside Dog Grooming 11555 Woodside Ave	562-0710
Su-Ets Kennels 10631 Prospect Ave	448-8760

SPRING VALLEY

Spring Valley Kennels & Cattery **9279 Campo Rd** *See our coupon*	**463-1722**

SOLANA BEACH

Charlies Canine Corner 574 Stevens Ave	755-5222
Perfect Pet 201 S Highway 101	755-3308
Rancho-Solana Pet Spa 247 S Highway 101	755-9318

SPRING VALLEY

Casa De Oro Pet Grooming 9905 Campo Rd	462-7300
Grooming By Joyce 577 Sweetwater Rd	464-4373
Mike's Aquarium & Pet Ctr 651 Sweetwater Rd	461-7661
Plaza Pet 9734 1/2 Campo Rd	466-6320
Rancho San Diego Dog Grooming 10783 Jamacha Blvd	670-4779
Spartan Kennels 3971 Spring Dr	461-5577
Spring Creek Kennel & Cattery 9279 Campo Rd	463-1722

VALLEY CENTER

Alibi Acres 16750 Paradise Mountain Rd	749-4100

VISTA

Ce Ce Belle Pet Hotel 29920 Margale Ln	758-7322
Club Pet Ba-Be-Loka's 857 E Vista Way	940-1851
Grooming By Alexis 857 E Vista Way	724-1708
Margale Kennels 29976 Margale Ln	726-3391
Mickey's K-9 Country Club 1920 Shadowridge Dr	727-1278
Spicer's Shaggy Dog 1929 W Vista Way	726-7387
Tails A Waggin 1528 N Santa Fe Ave	941-1991

FLEA & PEST CONTROL

BONITA
America's Finest City Pest   234-6129
Po Box 1062

CARLSBAD
Kennedy Pest Control Inc   434-5497
2725 Jefferson St # 2d

Pestmaster Services   729-1315
Po Box 4486

Terminix International   438-7768
2221 Las Palmas Dr

CHULA VISTA
Chula Vista Termite & Pest   425-3300
244 3rd Ave

Diamond Termite   420-5511
1251 3rd Ave

EL CAJON
A-All Pest Control Extrmntrs   440-5253
1456 N Magnolia Ave

Algon Exterminating Co   583-1881
13689 Highway 8 Business

Cartwright Termite & Pest Ctrl   286-1941
1376 Broadway

Dewey's Pest Control Co   443-7951
9386 Bond Ave

Jim's Horticultural Svc   447-0845
215 Lindell Ave

Pest Patrol Inc   442-7600
338 W Lexington Ave

Sunland Pest Control   442-5449
1290 Broadway

Terminix International   353-5381
457 N Cuyamaca St

Terminix International   593-1893
497 Vernon Way

Thomas Pest Control Co   442-9189
Po Box 1501

Uncle Mike's Pest Control   440-8451
7931 Winter Gardens Blvd

ENCINITAS
Holdsworth Pest Control   792-5231
Po Box 232754

Newlin Pest Control   433-2124

Terminix International   727-4650
630 Superior St

ESCONDIDO
A W Stone Termite & Pest Cntrl   743-2847
1539 Sterling Ct

American Insectaries   751-1436
31030 Rodriguez Rd

Antimite   745-7612
1570 S Escondido Blvd

Escondido Pest Control   741-5909
813 Harding St

Falcon Pest Control   741-0270
2410 Glenridge Rd

Fly Control Svc   747-6336
Jesmond Dene Rd

Newlin Pest Control   743-7611
10160 Quail Glen Way

Powell Termite & Pest Control   738-9051
Po Box 301415

Scherrer Termite & Pest Cntrl   741-8901
360 N Midway Dr

Stock Exterminators   632-0992
118 N Vinewood St

Sunland Pest Control   747-4404
Po Box 2113

Terminix International   489-0111
630 Superior St

Western Exterminator Co   741-3186
1936 Commercial St

FALLBROOK
Buggsy Sturtevant Control   728-4381
1139 E Mission Rd

Fallbrook Pest Control   (714) 676-2014
504 E Alvarado St # 102

LA JOLLA
Seacoast Termite Control   454-9563
7460 Girard Ave # 14

LA MESA
Aloha City Pest Control Inc   260-1730
7317 El Cajon Blvd # 203

Knott's Pest Control   466-0464
5141 Guild St

FLEA & PEST CONTROL
(continued)

Western Exterminator Co　463-8898
7232 University Ave

LAKESIDE
Diamond Termite　297-9300
12550 Woodside Ave

Landscape Pest Control Co　466-1021
11644 Moreno Ave

LEMON GROVE
Blizzard System　286-2444
6610 Federal Blvd

County-Wide Exterminating Co　469-9479
3468 Citrus St # A

NATIONAL CITY
Columbia Pest Control　264-6443
127 W 9th St

Dewey Pest Control　477-7190
324 Civic Center Dr

Terminix International　474-7292
2704 Transportation Ave # 20

OCEANSIDE
Antamite　724-2290
1931 Plaza Real

Antimite　753-8535
1931 Plaza Real

Bug's Be Dead　439-4425
3419 Townwood Ct

Calterm Exterminators　724-3411
1820 Peacock Blvd

Parkins Pest Control　941-1156
141 Nixon Cir

POWAY
Corky's Pest Control　748-6055
13031 Poway Rd

Orkin Pest Control　748-6599
12175 Flint Pl

S D County Pest & Termite Cntl　486-3762
14260 Garden Rd

Top Star Pest Control　237-9190
13061 Poway Rd

RAMONA
Richard L Stone Termite Cntrl　789-6006
709 D St # 205

SAN DIEGO
Advantage Pest Control　793-3532
11558 Sorrento Valley Rd # 1

Agricultural Pest Control Svc　536-2999
7766 Arjons Dr

All Cities Bee & Pest Control　565-8227
8280 Clairemont Mesa Blvd

American Pest Control Co　284-2633
3560 Fairmount Ave

Antimite Pest Control　231-2900
4017 42nd St

Bill's 3v Pest Control　264-0787
435 47th St

Bonita Pest Control　428-0576
2332 Mindanao Way

Bug Shooters　723-1607
9245 Dowdy Dr # 109

Castle Termite Co　283-6134
3617 Fairmount Ave

Centurion Pest Control　549-0708
Po Box 720266

Checkmate Exterminators　746-8383
Po Box 19914

Commercial Of Ca Pest Cntrl　521-0692
4382 44th St

D & S Termite Control　283-5577
3533 Fairmount Ave

Dewey Pest Control Co　272-3611
4623 De Soto St

Flea-X　1-800-773-5329
See our coupon　Or 233-5329

Flea Xperts　268-1822
8993 Complex Dr

Harbor Pest Control　584-4494
6160 Fairmount Ave

Household Pest Control　278-4884
3636 Fairmount Ave

Hydrex Pest Control Co　741-7141
9530 Dowdy Dr

Knight Termite & Pest Control　280-2400
4446 Vandever Ave

FLEA & PEST CONTROL
(continued)

Landscape Pest Control 3428 El Cajon Blvd # J	280-5242
Lloyd Termite Control 935 Sherman St	298-9865
Nationwide Pest Control Svc 5067 Glasgow Dr	275-4321
Pest Termite & Fumigation Svc 3636 Fairmount Ave	286-4543
Prism 4619 Mission Gorge Pl	583-2131
Pro Ex 9255 Towne Centre Dr	549-7074
Rick's Environmental Svc 11545 Sorrento Valley Rd # 302	455-9711
Terminix International 3675 Ruffin Rd # 330	268-3824
Terminix International 7630 Miramar Rd # 2200	486-9095
Terminix International 8282 Buckhorn St	495-0405
Top Star Pest Control 14309 Penasquitos Dr	486-4235
Truly Nolen Exterminating Inc 5909 Mission Gorge Rd	283-6251
Truly Nolen Of America 9815 Carroll Canyon Rd	695-3327
We-Got-Ya Pest Control 8448 Noeline Ln	280-0066

SAN MARCOS

All Best Extermintators 120 N Pacific St # B1	566-2102
Corky's Pest Control 133 N Pacific St # F	432-8801
Corky's Pest Control 909 Rancheros Dr	432-8801
Dewey Pest Control Co 1370 Grand Ave	753-1850
Lloyd Pest Control 223 S Bent Ave	436-4433
Pest-B-Dead 1036 Commerce St # D	632-1165
Sunland Pest Control 1046 Commerce St # B	436-1818
Truly Nolen Exterminating Inc 1310 Descanso Ave	744-7631

SANTEE

Deal Termite Co 9505 Jeremy St	562-8068
Eliminate Termite 10744 Rockville St	562-7900
Fortress Fumigation Co 10744 Rockville St	448-5636
L B Elms Complete Termite 10321 Woodpark Dr	448-0181
Mc Way Termite & Pest Control 10744 Rockville St	258-0993
Termite Inspector Inc 9530 Pathway St	562-6941

SPRING VALLEY

Aladdin Termite Control Po Box 33	463-2092
Corky's Pest Control 611 Ramona Ave	231-1636
Insect World Po Box 365	469-3321
Pestmaster Services 2820 Via Orange Way	265-1075
Southwood Pest Control 9051 Birch St	589-7773

VISTA

A A Same Day Exterminators 1330 N Melrose Dr # B	941-9880
Gemini Pest Control 1058 Taylor St	436-2271
Head Exterminators 1155 S Santa Fe Ave	753-6994
North County Exterminators 2540 S Santa Fe Ave	727-6500
Pinpoint Pest Control Po Box 1488	726-3809
Starwood Pest Control 1506 Alta Vista Dr	758-5050
Strike 3 Pest Control 2055 Thibodo Rd	598-1892

FLEA & PEST CONTROL
(continued)
Willis Exterminators 726-3088
1658 Mesa Verde Dr

HEALTHCARE - ALTERNATIVE
EL CAJON
Dr. Kevin May 444-9491
560 N. Johnson Ave

ENCINITAS
Dr. Michelle Drake 753-9393
681 Encinitas Blvd. #304f

FALLBROOK
Dr. Adriane Moore 723-6633

SAN DIEGO
Dr. Blake 484-3490
9888 Carmel Mountain Rd. #F

Dr. Robert Smatt 278-1575
5621 Balboa Ave.

Dr. Patricia Unger 584-8418
3817 Adams Ave.

Dr. Patrick Melese 292-6116
10799 Tierrasanta Blvd

HEALTHCARE - HOSPITALS
ALPINE
Alpine Animal Hospital 445-5683
3220 Alpine Blvd

Alpine Veterinary Hospital 445-6262
2113 Arnold Way

BONITA
Town & Country Animal Hospital 479-3311
4055 Bonita Rd

BONSALL
Bonsall Pet Hospital 630-1711
5519 Mission Rd # H

Vista Veterinary Hospital 724-7186
6009 W Lilac Rd

BORREGO SPRINGS
St Francis Animal Clinic 767-4559
2307 Stirrup Rd

CARDIFF BY SEA
Cardiff Animal Hospital
2159 San Elijo Ave 436-3215
See our coupon

CARLSBAD
Aardvark Animal Health Ctr 438-7766
6986 El Camino Real # I

All Cats Hospital 431-3585
7040 Avenida Encinas # 109

Carlsbad Animal Clinic 729-4431
2739 State St

El Camino Veterinary Hospital 729-3330
2505 S Vista Way

La Costa Animal Hospital 944-1266
7750 El Camino Real # G

CHULA VISTA
AAA Animal Hospital 420-6423
1280 3rd Ave

Amazon Pet & Bird Clinic 476-0053
1172 3rd Ave # D8

Bonita Pet Hospital Inc 427-2233
3438 Bonita Rd

CHULA VISTA
Chula Vista Veterinary Clinic 420-3984
80 Broadway

Melrose Pet Clinic 427-2851
1466 Melrose Ave

Otay Lakes Veterinary Clinic 482-2000
736 Otay Lakes Rd

Pet Clinic 422-0194
3326 Main St

South Bay Veterinary Hospital 422-6186
1038 Broadway

Telegraph Canyon Pet Clinic 421-1323
577 Telegraph Canyon Rd

CORONADO
Coronado Veterinary Hospital 435-6281
150 Orange Ave

CORONADO
Crown Veterinary Hospital 435-6624
817 Orange Ave

Directory

HEALTHCARE - HOSPITALS (continued)

DEL MAR
All Creatures Hospital 481-7992
3665 Via De La Valle

DEL MAR
Del Mar Heights Vet Hospital 792-3888
2626 Del Mar Heights Rd # B

DEL MAR
Del Mar Veterinary Hospital 755-9351
2132 Jimmy Durante Blvd

EL CAJON
Abbey Clinic For Cats 443-9707
8575 Los Coches Rd # 5

Abc Veterinary Hospital 590-6160
522 E Chase Ave

Agape Veterinary Hospital 447-8103
1291 N 2nd St

Animal Birth Control & Health 440-7888
522 E Chase Ave

Animal Care Clinic 670-8700
2650 Jamacha Rd # 159

Broadway Animal Hospital 444-1166
380 Broadway

Cajon Rancho Pet Hospital 442-5571
1682 Greenfield Dr

El Cajon Valley Veterinary 444-9491
560 N Johnson Ave

Jamacha Veterinary Clinic 579-0377
693 Jamacha Rd

Judy Veterinary Clinic 449-3500
1764 N 2nd St

Rancho San Diego Animal Hosp 660-6767
2990 Jamacha Rd # 176

Singing Hills Animal Hospital 441-5850
1951 Willow Glen Dr

Valhalla Veterinary Clinic
1498 Jamacha Rd # 104 440-4747
See our coupon

ENCINITAS
Encinitas Veterinary Clinic 753-1162
222 N Highway 101

Encinitas Village Vet Clinic 436-1080
119 N El Camino Real # B

House Calls 436-9944
Po Box 230293

North Coast Veterinary Medical 632-1072
285 N El Camino Real # 105

San Dieguito Vet Hospital Inc 753-9124
195 N El Camino Real

Santa Fe Plaza Animal Clinic 753-6512
421 Santa Fe Dr

Village Square Animal Hospital
1466 Encinitas Blvd 942-1220
See our coupon

Westlake Veterinary Clinic 753-9393
681 Encinitas Blvd # 304

ESCONDIDO
Aark Animal Hospital 745-5171
1326 Mission Rd

Acacia Animal Hospital 745-8115
1040 N Broadway

Animal Medical Hospital 741-8221
130 N Hale Ave

Ben P Maurer Animal Clinic 745-3252
2525 S Centre City Pky

Circle R Animal Clinic 749-7979
8751 Old Castle Rd

Companion Animal Clinic 743-2751
1215 S Escondido Blvd # A

Del Norte Plaza Vet Clinic
306 W El Norte Pky # F 741-8387
See our coupon

El Norte Veterinary Clinic 432-0400
1014 W El Norte Pky

Escondido Hills Animal Hosp 746-3647
555 W Country Club Ln # G

Escondido Small Animal Hosp 745-4515
630 Enterprise St

Hidden Valley Pet Clinic 746-4302
1906 E Valley Pky

Parkway Pet Clinic 743-0973
905 E Valley Pky

Sunset Pet Clinic 741-7729
1911 Sunset Dr

HEALTHCARE - HOSPITALS (continued)

Val-U-Vet & Pet Depot 738-0600
485 N Rose St

Village Veterinary Hospital 741-9999
316 W Mission Ave # 113

FALLBROOK

Alvarado Veterinary Hosptial 728-6606
347 E Alvarado St

Avocado Animal Hospital 728-5771
1111 E Mission Rd

Fallbrook Veterinary Hospital 728-8358
1216 S Main St

IMPERIAL BEACH

Imperial Beach Pet Hospital
538 12th St **424-3961**
See our coupon

Seacoast Pet Clinic 429-7387
600 Palm Ave # 103

JAMUL

Jamul Veterinary Clinic 669-1666
13910 Lyons Valley Rd # A

LA JOLLA

Animal Hospital Of La Jolla 459-2665
7601 Draper Ave

Bird Rock Animal Clinic 459-3279
5588 La Jolla Blvd

Nautilus Veterinary Clinic 454-0354
6911 La Jolla Blvd

LA MESA

A Pet Emergency Clinic 462-4800
5232 Jackson Dr # 105

Eastridge Veterinary Clinic 465-5291
7750 University Ave # A

El Cerrito Veterinary Hospital 466-0533
6911 University Ave

Fletcher Hills Pet Clinic 463-6604
9160 Fletcher Pky

Fuerte Animal Hospital 440-1432
4620 Avocado Blvd

Grossmont Animal Hospital 466-0501
8274 Parkway Dr # 100

Helix Pet Hospital 469-2129
4223 Palm Ave

La Mesa Pet Hospital 469-0138
5336 Jackson Dr

La Mesa-Jamul Pet Hospital 670-6278
3647 Avocado Blvd

Lake Murray Village Veterinary 464-3177
5644 Lake Murray Blvd

Parkway Pet Hospital 463-9151
8200 Parkway Dr

University Animal Clinic
7134 University Ave **463-9861**
See our coupon

LAKESIDE

Woodside Animal Hospital 561-5311
12149 Woodside Ave

LEMON GROVE

Lemon Grove Veterinary Hosp 463-0301
7572 North Ave

San Diego Pet Hospital 462-6600
7368 Broadway # A

Skyline Animal & Spay Clinic 464-8301
1860 Skyline Dr

OCEANSIDE

College Pet Clinic 631-2080
475 College Blvd # 8

Lone Star Veterinary Hospital 722-4840
3870 Mission Ave # D6

Mission Animal & Bird Hospital 433-3763
3308 Mission Ave

Mohnacky Animal Hospital 945-1000
3504 College Blvd # E

Oceanside Veterinary Hospital 757-1571
2960 San Luis Rey Rd

Pacific Animal Hospital 757-2442
2801 Oceanside Blvd

Rancho Del Oro Veterinary Hosp 945-0606
4093 Oceanside Blvd # J

Temple Heights Animal Hospital 630-3590
4750 Oceanside Blvd # A2

PINE VALLEY

Pine Valley Veterinary Clinic 473-8797
28914 Old Highway 80

Directory

HEALTHCARE - HOSPITALS (continued)

POWAY

Animal Medical Hospital 14031 Poway Rd	271-9711
Midland Animal Clinic Inc 14210 Midland Rd	748-4412
Poway Animal Hospital 12219 Poway Rd	748-3326
Poway Valley Animal Clinic 13027 Poway Rd	748-1447
Town & Country Veterinary Hosp 14034 Poway Rd	486-4800

RAMONA

Adobe Animal Hospital 1134 D St	789-7090
High Valley Veterinary Hosp 1029 D St	788-6250
Ramona Animal Hospital 1735 Main St # E	788-0960

RANCHO SANTA FE

Animal Care & Education Ctr 6461 El Apajo	756-3791
Veterinary Specialty Hospital 6525 Calle Del Nido	759-1777

SAN DIEGO

A Black Mt Rd Pet Clinic 13161 Black Mountain Rd # 1	484-5000
ABC Veterinary Hospitals 2032 Hornblend St	270-4120
ABC Veterinary Hospitals 8020 Ronson Rd	278-1825
All Care Cat Hospital 4680 Clairemont Mesa Blvd	274-2287
American Animal Hospital 8135 Mira Mesa Blvd # 2	457-5111
Angel Animal Clinic-North Park 3537 30th St	291-0042
Animal Emergency Clinic 13240 Evening Creek Dr S	748-7387
Animals Of San Diego 246 W Washington St	295-1008
Ark Animal Hospital 6171 Balboa Ave	277-3665
Balboa Veterinary Hospital 7931 Balboa Ave	279-0425
Ballast Point Veterinary Clinic 140 Sylvester Rd Bldg 210	224-3080
Bay Park Pet Clinic Inc 1102 Morena Blvd	276-1616
Bernardo Heights Veterinary 15721 Bernardo Heights Pky # K	485-9111
Boulevard Animal Clinic 7047 El Cajon Blvd	582-7250
Cabrillo Veterinary Hospital 4138 Voltaire St	225-9684
Carmel Mountain Animal Hosp 9888 Carmel Mountain Rd # F	484-3490
Carmel Mountain Ranch Vet Hosp 11925 Carmel Mountain Rd # 802	592-9779
Carmel Valley Pet Clinic 3890 Valley Center Dr # 101	259-8881
Center Veterinary Clinic 8977 Mira Mesa Blvd	271-1152
Cheshire Cat Clinic 1945 Garnet Ave # B	483-1573
Clairemont Animal Hospital 2926 Garnet Ave	273-0224
Clairemont Square Animal Hosp 4941 Clairemont Sq # G	274-1760
Clairemont Village Pet Clinic 3007 Clairemont Dr # G	275-5752
Colina Veterinary Hospital 5530 University Ave	286-3360
College Animal Hospital 5653 El Cajon Blvd	286-1980
Colony Veterinary Clinic 7748 Regents Rd # 302	450-5047
Emergency Animal Clinic 2317 Hotel Cir S	299-2400
Friars Road Pet Hospital 10433 Friars Rd # G	282-7677
Genesee Bird & Pet Clinic 5621 Balboa Ave	278-1575

HEALTHCARE - HOSPITALS (continued)

Golden Triangle Veterinary Svc 3961 Governor Dr	453-6757
Governor Animal Clinic 3218 Governor Dr	453-6312
Grand Animal Hospital 1033 Grand Ave	272-1320
Hillcrest Veterinary Hospital 3949 1st Ave	298-7714
Kearny Mesa Veterinary Hospital 7677 Ronson Rd # 100	278-0171
Kensington Veterinary Hospital 3817 Adams Ave	584-8418
Main Street Small Animal Hospital 2773 Main St	232-7401
Mesa Pet Hospital 8330 Ronson Rd	279-3000
Mira Mesa Pet Clinic 9396 Mira Mesa Blvd # A	271-5515
Mission Gorge Animal Hospital 6690 Mission Gorge Rd # M	280-1503
Mission Valley Pet Clinic 4329 Twain Ave	281-2934
Morena Pet Hospital & Bird Ctr 1540 Morena Blvd	275-0888
North Park-Pacific Veterinary 2646 University Ave	295-9025
North Park Veterinary Hospital 4054 Normal St	299-6020
Pacific Beach Veterinary Clinic 1362 Garnet Ave	272-6255
Pacific Highway Pet Clinic 3895 Pacific Hwy	295-4231
Pacific Petcare Veterinary 12720 Carmel Country Rd	481-1101
Pacific Veterinary Svc 2646 University Ave	295-2287
Palm Ridge Pet Hospital 4370 Palm Ave # S	690-2272
Penasquito Pet Clinic 9728 Carmel Mtn. Rd # E *See our coupon*	484-1260
Peninsula Veterinary Clinic 3767 Voltaire St	223-7145
Plaza Bernardo Animal Hospital 16769 Bernardo Center Dr # K28	451-0990
Point Loma Veterinary Clinic 2158 Catalina Blvd	222-4482
Presidio Veterinary Clinic 5427 Linda Vista Rd	297-0219
Rancho Bernardo Vet Clinic 12540 Oaks North Dr # D	487-4130
Rancho Mesa Animal Hospital 8710 Miramar Rd	566-0422
Rancho San Carlos Pet Clinic 7850 Golfcrest Dr	462-6820
Renaissance Veterinary Clinic 8915 Towne Centre Dr # 110	452-7100
Rose Canyon Animal Hospital 4295 Jutland Dr	273-4680
Rosecrans Pet Hospital 3786 Rosecrans St	297-3857
San Carlos Veterinary Hospital 8618 Lake Murray Blvd	460-3100
Scripps Ranch Veterinary Hosp 9990 Scripps Ranch Blvd	566-4912
Shelter Island Vet Clinic 1270 Scott St	222-0597
South San Diego Vet Hosp 2910 Coronado Ave	423-7121
Spay-Neuter Clinic 5530 University Ave	286-3383
Sunset Cliffs Animal Clinic 4741 Point Loma Ave	224-0773
Tierramesa Veterinary Clinic 9353 Clairemont Mesa Blvd # Q	268-0044
Tierrasanta Pet Hospital 6030 Santo Rd # A	569-7777
Turquoise Animal Hospital 950 Turquoise St	488-0658
Uptown Veterinary Clinic 4054 Normal St	293-3726
Veterinary Surgical Specialist 2317 Hotel Cir S	560-8006

Directory

HEALTHCARE - HOSPITALS (continued)

Westwood Bernardo Veterinary 485-7570
11605 Duenda Rd # D

SAN MARCOS

ABC Veterinary Clinic 471-4950
330 Rancheros Dr # A

Cranney Veterinary Svc Inc 471-1389
3427 N Twin Oaks Valley Rd

Family Pets Medical Ctr 744-7559
997 W San Marcos Blvd # 102a

Levitt Animal Hospital 744-5242
1155 Grand Ave

Palomar Animal Hospital 727-7622
2615 S Santa Fe Ave

San Marcos Animal Medical Ctr 744-7410
325 S Rancho Santa Fe Rd # D

San Marcos Veterinary Clinic 744-5400
145 S Rancho Santa Fe Rd

SANTEE

Mast Boulevard Pet Care Ctr 448-6490
9740 N Magnolia Ave

Mission Gorge Veterinary Hosp 258-1150
9302 Carlton Hills Blvd

Santee Pet Hospital 449-4100
8936 Carlton Hills Blvd

SOLANA BEACH

Academy Animal Hospital 755-1511
741 Academy Dr

SPRING VALLEY

Animal Medical Hospital 464-5125
704 Grand Ave

Paradise Valley Pet Hospital 263-0345
8360 Paradise Valley Rd # B

Spring Valley Veterinary 660-1114
9973 Campo Rd

VALLEY CENTER

Countryside Veterinary Clinic 749-3656
28746 Valley Center Rd

Valley Center Vet Clinic 749-0560
14219 Cool Valley Rd

VISTA

Alta Mira Animal Hospital 726-8918
998 S Santa Fe Ave

Brengle Terrace Animal Hosp 758-8004
971 Vale Terrace Dr

Cal-Vista Animal Hospital 726-3222
1318 N Santa Fe Ave

East Vista Pet Clinic 724-8313
2020 E Vista Way

Emergency Animal Clinic 724-7444
1925 W Vista Way

Melrose Veterinary Clinic 727-5151
1680 S Melrose Dr # 104

Pet Medical Center 598-2222
619 Sycamore Ave

Shadowridge Village Vet Clinic 727-7900
751 Shadowridge Dr

Tri-City Vet Clinic & Boarding 758-2091
1929 W Vista Way # J

Vista Veterinary Hospital 726-1234
1139 S Santa Fe Ave

HEALTHCARE - POISON CONTROL

Poison Control Hotline 800-544-4404

Poison Control 800-548-2423
National Animal Control Poison Center ($30)

Poison Control 900-680-0000
National Animal Control Poison Center ($20)

HEALTHCARE - SPECIALISTS

ANESTHESIOLOGY

LA JOLLA
Fujimoto, Jennifer 534-8612
Ucsd - La Jolla

DENTISTRY

SAN DIEGO
Mulligan, Thomas 232-7401

RANCHO SANTA FE
Gilbert, Patricia 756-0790

HEALTHCARE - SPECIALISTS (continued)
SAN DIEGO
Griffin, Craig	560-9393
Rosenkrantz, Wayne	560-9393

HOSPITALS
SAN DIEGO
Animal Dermatology Clinic 13240 Evening Creek Dr S # 302	486-4600
Animal Internal Medicine 13240 Evening Creek Dr S # 302	486-3731
Eye Clinic For Animals 2317 Hotel Cir S	293-7055

INTERNAL MEDICINE
LA JOLLA
Shelton, Diane, Phd Ucsd - La Jolla	534-1537

LA MESA
Duesberg, Cynthia	462-4800

PHOENIX
Greene, Russel, Phd	800-592-0503

RANCHO SANTA FE
Hart, John	759-0790
Hill, Steve	759-0790
Humber, Kent	759-9131
Richter, Keith	756-0790

SAN DIEGO
Ford, Sara	299-2400
Kortz, Gregg, Neurology	299-2400
Slusser, Peter	560-7778

OPHTHALMOLOGY
SAN DIEGO
Macmillan, Alan	293-7055
Nelson, Darien	293-7055

PATHOLOGY
BRAWLEY
Howard, James	344-5738

PRACTITIONERS
FOUNTAIN VALLEY
Rooks, Robert, Canine/Feline	714-963-0909

OCEANSIDE
Atkinson, Al, Companion Animal	722-4840

SAN DIEGO
Jenkins, Jeff, Avian	260-1412

RADIOLOGY
CARDIFF
Hager, David, Md	943-1474

ENCINITAS
Craychee, Therese	943-0459

FALLBROOK
Rantanen, Norman	972-8662

HEALTHCARE -SPECIALISTS SURGERY
EL CAJON
Hampel, Nancy	444-1166

ESCONDIDO
Garcia, Maura	745-8115

FOUNTAIN VALLEY
Rooks, Robert	714-963-0909

RANCHO SANTA FE
Richardson, Lynn	756-0818

SAN DIEGO
Botte, Robert	229-0777
Gahring, Dean	460-3100
Lenehan, Timothy	560-8006
Mullen, Holly	299-2400
Tarvin, Guy	560-8006

WOODLAND HILLS
Henry, Jack	818-513-4583

ZOOLOGICAL MEDICINE
ESCONDIDO
Ensley, Philip	735-5503

LA JOLLA
Robinson, Phillip UCSD - La Jolla	534-6064

HEALTHCARE - VETERINARIANS

ALPINE

A Lynn Dvm 445-5683
3220 Alpine Blvd

Carlton R Kibbee Dvm 445-4444
3326 Otto Ave

BONITA

Gary J Amaral Dvm 267-7775
4033 Allen School Rd

James T Dowe Dvm 479-3311
4055 Bonita Rd

BONSALL

Colburn Veterinary Svc 728-2319
Po Box 750

CARDIFF BY SEA

Katherine Allen Dvm 436-3215
2159 San Elijo Ave Dvm

Monica Laflin 436-3215
2159 San Elijo Ave

Susan Redpath Dvm 436-3215
2159 San Elijo Ave

CARLSBAD

Edward S Attix Dvm 729-4431
2739 State St

Ellie Wattles Dvm 729-3330
2505 S Vista Way

James Palenscar Dvm 729-4431
2739 State St

Ronald J Magrini Dvm 434-2410
Po Box 850

CHULA VISTA

D E Tomblin Dvm 427-2233
3438 Bonita Rd

James G Valentine Dvm 427-2233
3438 Bonita Rd

CORONADO

Lisa Rehberger Dvm 435-6624
817 Orange Ave

DEL MAR

David R Martin Dvm 481-7992
3665 Via De La Valle

Jean Hamilton Dvm 481-7992
3665 Via De La Valle

Mary Gibbs Dvm 481-7992
3665 Via De La Valle

R A Roland-Holst Dvm 755-9351
2132 Jimmy Durante Blvd

EL CAJON

Celeste Benavides Dvm 444-9491
560 N Johnson Ave

Craig L Chandler Dvm 561-4661
10312 Quail Canyon Rd

Dave Naidus Dvm 444-1166
380 Broadway

David A Knox Dvm 440-4747
1498 Jamacha Rd # 104

Douglas J Paulson Dvm 444-9491
560 N Johnson Ave

Kenneth Porte Dvm 444-1166
380 Broadway

Kevin May Dvm 444-9491
560 N Johnson Ave

Kim K Sergent Dvm 561-4661
10312 Quail Canyon Rd

Lanny H Cornell Dvm 441-5850
1951 Willow Glen Dr

Larry Martin Dvm 660-1991
2650 Jamacha Rd # 159

Mary Mc Lain Dvm 440-4747
1498 Jamacha Rd # 104

Nancy Hampel Dvm 444-1166
380 Broadway

Terry Pollock Dvm 444-1166
380 Broadway

ENCINITAS

Christine Ross Dvm 755-0306
815 S Escondido Blvd

Colleen A Fancher Dvm 436-9944
Po Box 230293

John Newcomb Dvm 944-0910
770 Rancho Santa Fe Rd # A

Nancy Bushnell 942-1220
1466 Encinitas Blvd.

HEALTHCARE - VETERINARIANS (continued)

Peter Dowell Dvm   634-0545
Po Box 231185

Ranch & Coast Equine   942-2884
1306 El Camino Ct

ESCONDIDO

Alice Vranes Dvm   743-0973
905 E Valley Pky

Christine Sherer Dvm   741-9999
316 W Mission Ave # 113

Geoffrey R Smith Dvm   745-5171
1326 Mission Rd

Maura K Wallace Dvm   745-8115
1040 N Broadway

Rick Lindbeck   741-8387
306-F West El Norte Pkwy.

Roberta H Syme Dvm   743-2751
1215 S Escondido Blvd # A

FALLBROOK

Casey Brechtel Dvm   942-2884
2265 Mardavido Ln

Joanne P Thacher Dvm   723-7747
1706 Rainbow Valley Blvd

IMPERIAL BEACH

Jo Beaty Dvm   424-3961
538 12th St

LA JOLLA

Chari L Hutchroft Dvm   454-6155
7520 Fay Ave

Marilyn K Seals Dvm   454-6155
7520 Fay Ave

Morizi & Morizi   459-2665
7601 Draper Ave

Sue Morizi Dvm   459-2665
7601 Draper Ave

Valerie W Ewell Dvm   454-6155
7520 Fay Ave

LA MESA

Harold A Stephens Dvm   463-6604
9160 Fletcher Pky

James P Thomas Dvm   463-9151
8200 Parkway Dr

Julie A Massey Dvm   466-0533
6911 University Ave

Margaret Lake Dvm   670-6278
3647 Avocado Blvd

Robert E. Larrson   463-9861
7134 University Ave.

OCEANSIDE

Dennis Dereig Dvm   757-2442
2801 Oceanside Blvd

Gary Siebert Dvm   433-3763
3308 Mission Ave

James Palenscar Dvm   757-2442
2801 Oceanside Blvd

Lauren Bauer Dvm   757-2442
2801 Oceanside Blvd

Paul Weber Dvm   757-2442
2801 Oceanside Blvd

Sonja Lindberg Dvm   630-3590
4750 Oceanside Blvd # A2

PAUMA VALLEY

Pauma Valley Mobile Veterinary   742-4500
Po Box 1262

Scott R Haskell Dvm   742-4500
Po Box 1262

POWAY

Connie L Stapleton Dvm   271-9711
14031 Poway Rd

George K Shinzaki Dvm   695-3407
12219 Poway Rd

Hugh N Weech & Assoc   271-4666
13027 Poway Rd

Norman K Switzer Dvm   566-0411
14210 Midland Rd

RAMONA

Christopher George Dvm   789-5120
1357 Barnett Rd

Keith Hilinski Dvm   789-7090
1134 D St

RANCHO SANTA FE

Anne E Mc Cabe Dvm   759-2772
6525 Calle Del Nido

Keith P Richter Dvm   759-1777
6525 Calle Del Nido St

Directory

HEALTHCARE - VETERINARIANS (continued)

Lisa Grim Dvm 759-9964
6525 Calle Del Nido # F

Patricia A Gilbert Dvm 759-1777
6525 Calle Del Nido St

Paul Mc Clellen Dvm 759-9964
6525 Calle Del Nido # F

Sara L Ford Dvm 759-1777
6525 Calle Del Nido St

SAN DIEGO

Andrew S Loar Dvm 296-7381
2317 Hotel Cir S

Ann E Stacker Dvm 286-3360
5530 University Ave

Anthony D Michael Dvm 273-0224
2926 Garnet Ave

Benita I Keiss Dvm 272-6255
1362 Garnet Ave

Bruce Cauble Dvm 279-3000
8330 Ronson Rd

Bruce N Persky Dvm 460-3100
8618 Lake Murray Blvd

C Kirk Feinberg Dvm 453-6312
3218 Governor Dr

Darien Nelson Dvm 293-7055
2317 Hotel Cir S

Deborah Harvazinski Dvm 272-6255
1362 Garnet Ave

Hans T Ewertz Dvm 223-7145
3767 Voltaire St

Helen Green Dvm 299-6020
4054 Normal St

Janet Loken Dvm 690-2272
4370 Palm Ave # S

John C Boyd Dvm 481-1101
12720 Carmel Country Rd

Laura Stadtmore Dvm 450-5047
7748 Regents Rd # 302

Marla Saltzman Dvm 460-3100
8618 Lake Murray Blvd

Michael Weber Dvm 270-4120
2032 Hornblend St

Mona Boord Dvm 486-4600
13240 Evening Creek Dr S # 302

Nanette Leto Dvm 270-4120
2032 Hornblend St

Patricia Carter Dvm 566-0422
8710 Miramar Rd

Robert J Botte Dvm 229-0777
1945 Garnet Ave

Robert Johnson Dvm 286-3360
5530 University Ave

Robert K Tugend Dvm 232-7401
2773 Main St

Ronald A May Dvm 270-4120
2032 Hornblend St

Sharon Sprouse, Dvm 484-1260
9728 Carmel Mtn. Rd.

Stan Kus Dvm 460-3100
8618 Lake Murray Blvd

Thomas W Mulligan Dvm 232-7401
2773 Main St

Timothy M Lenehan Dvm 299-2652
2317 Hotel Cir S

Victoria L Jordan Dvm 584-8418
3817 Adams Ave

Wayne Rosenkrantz Dvm 486-4600
13240 Evening Creek Dr S # 302

SAN MARCOS

Bill Talbot Dvm 471-1389
3427 N Twin Oaks Valley Rd

SOLANA BEACH

Harry H Hill Dvm 755-1511
741 Academy Dr

SPRING VALLEY

Christine Chapman Dvm 660-1114
9973 Campo Rd

Janet Loken Dvm 475-9770
8360 Paradise Valley Rd # B

Stanley Clemmensen Dvm 475-9770
8360 Paradise Valley Rd # B

VISTA

A K Statt Dvm 726-3222
1318 N Santa Fe Ave

HEALTHCARE - VETERINARIANS (continued)

Donna L Stevens Dvm   945-0177
Po Box 310

ID TAGS
SAN DIEGO
Lucky Pet   800-543-8247

Pet Tags   800-910-3263

Vet Tags   800-443-8247

LOCAL CLUBS - ALL BREED CLUBS
Bahia Sur Kennel Club Of Chula Vista
PO Box 877, Chula Vista, CA. 91910

Silver Bay Kennel Club Of San Diego
13553 Avenida Del Charro, El Cajon, CA. 92021

Mt. Palomar Kennel Club
3719 Via Las Villas, Oceanside, CA. 92056

Del Sur Kennel Club
1424 Jethrow Way, El Cajon, CA. 92109

AGILITY CLUBS
Agility Club Of San Diego   561-2434

CAT CLUBS
San Diego Cat Fanciers (Cat Fanciers' Association Affiliate)   295-5422

Southern California Cat Club
4095 #4 Harrison St, Carlsbad, CA. 92008

FIELD TRIAL & HUNTING CLUBS
San Diego Hunting & Retrieving Club 689-2573

San Diego Sporting Dog Club   583-8392

HERDING
Blazin' Border Collies   739-8673

Herding Breed Club Of San Diego   484-4377

Whiskers 'N Wool   442-7640

German Shepard Dog Club Of San Diego
PO Box 1828, Julian, CA. 92036

San Diego Collie Club
3664 Budd St, San Diego, CA. 92111

Shetland Sheepdog Club Of San Diego
16333 Bassett Ct, Ramona, CA. 92065

Pembroke Welsch Corgi Club Of S. Cal.
30310 Miller Rd., Valley Center, CA. 92082

HOUND GROUP CLUBS
San Diego Dachsund Club, Inc.
1170 Denver Lane B, El Cajon, CA. 92921

Greater San Diego Basset Hound Club
894 Helix Ave., Chula Vista, CA. 91911

Boxer Club Of San Diego County
1809 Oak Hill Dr., Escondido, CA. 92027

Aztec Doberman Pinscher Club
9365 Single Oak Dr., Lakeside, CA. 92040

Greater San Diego Whippet Club
1104 5th St., National City, CA. 91950

NON-SPORTING GROUPS
Bichon Frise Club Of San Diego
5769 Beaumont Ave, La Jolla, CA. 92037

Bulldog Club Of Greater San Diego
1440 Pepper Dr, El Cajon, CA. 92921

San Diego Lhasa Apso Club
6517 Mt Ackerman Dr, San Diego, CA. 92111

San Diego Poodle Club
Po Box 336, Bonita, CA. 91908

The Dalmatian Club Of San Diego County Is A Group Of Breeders, Owners, And Enthusiasts Promoting Welfare And Camaraderie At Club Functions, Shows, And Matches In Accordance With AKC Regulations.   561-7382

OBEDIENCE CLUBS
Obedience Club Of San Diego   273-5034
14640 Lyons Valley Rd., Jamul, CA. 91935

All Breed Obedience Club   287-2211

Hidden Valley Obedience Club
409 S Tulip, Escondido, CA.. 92025

LOCAL CLUBS -
(CONTINUED)

SCHUTZHUND CLUBS
Big West 956-3647

San Diego Diensthund 264-1796
4918 Dalehaven Place, San Diego, CA. 92105

San Diego Schutzhund 789-4494
Po. Box 446, Ramona, CA. 92065

Aztec Schutzhund Club 674-1436
17382 Caminto Masada, Sd. CA. 92127

North County Schutzhund Club 726-3684
628 Mar Vista Dr. San Diego, CA. 92083

O.G. Binnenland Schutzhund Club 789-7624
856 Schoolhouse Rd. Ramona, CA. 92065

SPORTING GROUP CLUBS
English Cocker Spaniel Club Of San Diego
3505 Alpine Blvd., Alpine, CA. 91901

German Shorthaired Pointer Club Of San Diego 16922 Rio Maria Rd., Lakeside, CA. 92040

Cocker Spaniel Club Of San Diego 266-8754
12296 Ragweed St, San Diego, Ca 92129

Golden Retriever Club Of San Diego
6206 Lake Albano Ave, San Diego, Ca 92119

Irish Setter Club Of San Diego
Po Box 778, Ramona, CA. 92065

San Diego Brittany Club, Inc.
1477 Quest Rd, Ramona, CA. 92065

TERRIER GROUP CLUBS
Cairn Terrier Club Of S. California
889 El Paisano Dr., Fallbrook, CA. 92028

Miniature Schnauzer Club Of S. California
2918 Campos Dr., Fallbrook, CA. 92928

TERRIER GROUP CLUBS
Bedlington Terrier Club Of The West
632 El Norte Hills Pl, Escondido, CA. 92027

West Highland White Terrier Club Of Ca
1490 F Gustavo St., El Cajon, CA. 92019

TOY GROUP CLUBS
San Diego Pomeranian Club
2981 Calle Cumbre, San Diego, CA. 92139

WORKING GROUP CLUBS
Southern California Portuguese Water Dog Club 693 Shadowtree Dr., Oceanside, CA. 92054

Boxer Club Of San Diego County, Inc.
1809 Oak Hill Dr, Escondido, CA. 92027

Great Dane Club Of San Diego
4314 Pt Reyes Ct, Carlsbad, CA. 92008

Samoyed Club Of San Diego
4420 Lowell St, La Mesa, CA. 91944

St. Bernard Club Of San Diego
29853 Disney Ln, Vista, CA. 92084

SW Rottweiler Club Of San Diego
6310 Scimitar Dr, San Diego, CA. 92114

PARKS, BEACHS & TRAILS
See Page....18

PET LOSS - BEREAVEMENT COUNSELING
SAN DIEGO

Colorado State University 303-221-4535
College Of Vet. Med.

The Animal Medical Center 212-838-8100
New York City

The University Of Pennsylvania 215-898-4525
School Of Vet. Med.

University Of California 916-752-7418
School Of Vet. Med.

University Of Minnesota 612-624-4747
College Of Vet. Med.

Washington State University 509-335-1297
College Of Vet. Med.

PET LOSS - CEMETARIES
SAN DIEGO

A A Sorrento Valley Pet Cemtry   276-3361
10801 Sorrento Valley Rd

Parkside Group   275-0728
4295 Gesner St # 3b

San Diego Pet Memorial Park   271-4242
8995 Crestmar Pt

PET LOSS - PET LOSS SUPPORT
SAN DIEGO

Pet Loss Support Hotlines   517-483-2692
College Of Vet Med At Michigan

Pet Loss Support Hotlines   708-603-3884
Chicago Vet Med Assoc

Pet Loss Support Hotlines   904-392-4700
Univ Or Fl At Gainesville College

Pet Loss Support Hotlines   916-752-4200
Univ Of Ca At Davis

PHOTOGRAPHY
CHULA VISTA

Petsmart   656-0071
820 Paseo Del Rey

EL CAJON

Petsmart   442-0600
865 Jackman St.

SAN DIEGO

Petsmart   571-0300
3396 Murphy Canyon Rd

VISTA

Petsmart   630-3544
1740 University Dr.

RETAIL - PET SUPPLIES
ALPINE

Alpine Animal Jungle   445-4022
1730 Alpine Blvd # 116

Alpine Creek Pets   445-6868
1347 Tavern Rd # 16

CARDIFF BY SEA

Sholyn Kennels   942-8668
Po Box 1077

CARLSBAD

Animal Environments   438-4442
2270 Camino Vida Roble

Fortune's Grooming Salon   436-2442
7750 El Camino Real

Karen's Custom Grooming   431-7553
7130 Avenida Encinas # 100

Pee Dee's Paw Protectors
7416 Altiva Place   438-8226
See our coupon

Sun Pet Ctr   729-5941
2525 El Camino Real

Wesco Pet Supplies   434-0930
2855 Roosevelt St

CHULA VISTA

Dog Gallery   472-1777
1172 3rd Ave # D8

Petco Animal Supplies Inc   425-8853
1215 Broadway

Petco Animal Supplies Inc   427-2112
11 4th Ave

Petland Inc   482-7712
585 Telegraph Canyon Rd

Petmart   422-8178
368 E H St

Petsmart   656-0071
820 Paseo Del Rey

CORONADO

Village Pets   435-3513
945 Orange Ave

DEL MAR

All Creatures Hospital   481-7992
3665 Via De La Valle

Dexter's Deli
1229 Camino Del Mar   792-3707
See our coupon

Mary's Tack & Feed   755-2015
3675 Via De La Valle

RETAIL - PET SUPPLIES (CONTINUED)

EL CAJON

Animal House Grooming Shop 1286 Greenfield Dr	442-7387
Birdwood Kennels 1329 E Chase Ave	447-8020
Classy Canine School Of Dog 723 E Bradley Ave	449-4443
El Cajon Pet 1255 E Main St # A	444-2303
Glenview Feed Co 13283 Highway 8 Business	443-3883
Parkway Pet Ctr 509 Parkway Plz	442-0281
Pet Supply Warehouse 540 N 2nd St	441-5200
Petco 2510 Jamacha Rd	670-9688
Petco Animal Supplies Inc 796 Fletcher Pky	447-9907
Petco Animal Supplies Inc 2990 Jamacha Rd # 132	670-9688
Petmart 2864 Fletcher Pky	466-3474
Rancho San Diego Animal Hosp 2990 Jamacha Rd # 176	660-6767
Solid Gold Holistic Animal Ctr 1483 N Cuyamaca St	258-1914
Tender Loving Care Dog Groom 1428 Broadway	447-6585
Vets-Pets 1265 Avocado Ave # 103	589-2215
Vets Pets 522 E Chase Ave	469-3474
Petsmart 865 Jackman St.	442-0600

ENCINITAS

Animal Keeper 155 Saxony Rd	753-9366
Best Pets Ctr 270 N El Camino Real	436-1226
H & H Tack & Feed Co 1985 Olivenhain Rd	753-8050
Loving Care Pet Grooming 555 2nd St	436-1635
Paws & Claws 1403 Encinitas Blvd # D	634-1200
Pet People 123 N El Camino Real	634-1712
Petco Animal Supplies Inc 208 N El Camino Real	436-4121
Petmart 425 1/2 Santa Fe Dr	944-1819
Rancho Coastal Humane Society 389 Requeza St	753-6413
Santa Fe Plaza Animal Clinic 421 Santa Fe Dr	753-6512

ESCONDIDO

4 Feet & Feathers Pet Store 1835 S Centre City Pky # G	480-0858
Animal Emporium 1497 E Valley Pky	480-2971
California Pets 200 E Via Rancho Pky	741-7387
Cathy's Canine Salon & Btq 2205 E Valley Pky	745-1700
Cold Nose Grooming Salon 254 W 8th Ave	741-2707
Critter Corner 316 W Mission Ave # 117	746-5422
El Norte Pets 322 W El Norte Pky	747-8337
Escondido Feed & Supply 649 Rock Springs Rd	745-2911
Petco Animal Supplies Inc 1270 Auto Park Way	743-4352
Petco Animal Supplies Inc 1270 Valley Pky	743-4352
Petmart 1356 W Valley Pky	739-1375
Raining Cats & Dogs 191 Sunset Dr	743-0136

RETAIL - PET SUPPLIES (CONTINUED)

FALLBROOK
Creature Comforts   723-1411
520 S Main St

LA JOLLA
AAA Pet Professionals   456-1552
6905 La Jolla Blvd

La Jolla Paws Pet Supply   459-6614
7514 Girard Ave

Village Pet Shop   454-5449
5622 La Jolla Blvd

LA MESA
Doggie Depot   697-8565
6165 Lake Murray Blvd

El Cerrito Veterinary Hospital   466-0533
6911 University Ave

Great Danes   465-9507
9490 Loren Dr

Pet Outfitters   698-4056
6101 Lake Murray Blvd

Petco Animal Supplies Inc   469-2117
8693 La Mesa Blvd

Petmart   670-4402
3735 Avocado Blvd

LAKESIDE
Animal Antics   561-9727
9838 Channel Rd

Greyhound Pets Of America   443-0940
11404 Highway 67

Petco Animal Supplies Inc   561-0411
10137 Maine Ave

LEMON GROVE
Dave's Feed Stop   462-3434
3655 Costa Bella St

Lemon Grove Pets   460-1963
7116 Broadway

NATIONAL CITY
Fiesta Pet Shop   477-5997
1145 Highland Ave # A

Pet Plaza   477-4076
911 E Plaza Blvd

OCEANSIDE
Discount Pet Mart   967-7387
3915 Mission Ave

Oceana Pet Stop   439-6060
563 Vista Bella

Pacific Animal Hospital   757-2442
2801 Oceanside Blvd

Pet People   630-6130
4170 Oceanside Blvd

Petco Animal Supplies Inc   721-2114
2227 S El Camino Real

POWAY
Animal Supplies Of Poway   486-0170
12642 Poway Rd

Pet Supply Warehouse   679-2020
13375 Poway Rd

Petco Animal Supplies Inc   748-6876
12305 Poway Rd

Poway Pets   748-2424
14867 Pomerado Rd

RAMONA
Animal Pharm   788-0286
1668 Main St # S

SAN DIEGO
Adams Ave Pet Store   283-1867
3375 Adams Ave

Always Natural   **530-0532**
Free Home Delivery of pet foods & supplies *See our coupon*

Animal House Pet Store   295-8834
2726 University Ave

Animals Of San Diego   295-1008
246 W Washington St

Balboa Veterinary Hospital   279-0425
7931 Balboa Ave

Better Grooming   272-4301
4804 Gallatin Way

Cabrillo Veterinary Hospital   225-9684
4138 Voltaire St

Canine Castle   571-1225
9353 Clairemont Mesa Blvd

Casa De Pets   292-7387
10615 Tierrasanta Blvd # D

RETAIL - PET SUPPLIES (CONTINUED)

Dog Beach Dog Wash 4933 Voltaire St # C	523-1700
Dog House Factory 2251 Cecelia Ter	276-4439
Mutt Hutt 3256 Greyling Dr	576-9714
Newport Pet Shop 4896 Newport Ave	224-6151
Pacific Beach Pet Salon 1964 Garnet Ave	274-8844
Penasquitos Pets 13223 Black Mountain Rd	484-3809
Pet Deco 8736 Lake Murray Blvd	466-9681
Pet Express **Free Delivery of Fine Pet Foods** *See our coupon*	**1-800-735-Pets**
Pet Kingdom 3191 Sports Arena Blvd	224-2841
Pet Metro 3994 Clairemont Mesa Blvd # A	483-4100
Pet Pawlor 12540 Oaks North Dr	673-1777
Pet People 1786 Garnet Ave	270-3499
Pet People 5671 Balboa Ave	495-0333
Pet Supply Warehouse 1210 W Morena Blvd	275-5100
Pet Works 4505 La Jolla Village Dr	458-9981
Pet Xtra 7805 Arjons Dr	693-3639
Pet Zone 4266 University Ave	283-1812
Petco Animal Supplies Inc 3350 Sports Arena Blvd	223-2581
Petco Animal Supplies Inc 10450 Friars Rd	282-2104
Petco Animal Supplies Inc 5440 Clairemont Mesa Blvd	292-4283
Petco Animal Supplies Inc 9151 Rehco Rd	453-7845
Petco Animal Supplies Inc 1945 Garnet Ave # B	483-5821
Petco Animal Supplies Inc 11965 Bernardo Plaza Dr	673-5914
Petco Animal Supplies Inc 9420 Mira Mesa Blvd	695-2117
Petco Stores 10410 Friars Rd	563-0071
Petland Grooming 5430 Clairemont Mesa Blvd # D	268-3721
Petsmart 3396 Murphy Canyon Rd	571-0300
Petmart 2884 University Ave	297-3474
Petpals 11835 Carmel Mountain # 1301	673-9600
Petmart 9166 Mira Mesa Blvd	695-3655
Petmart Disc Pet Supls 645 Saturn Blvd # B	575-7387
Petmart Discount Pet Supplies 6363 El Cajon Blvd	286-3474
Petpeople 3625 Midway Dr	523-0552
Pink Poodle 4651 College Ave	583-2261
Poochies Self Svc Pet Wash Bar 6030 Santo Rd	541-2663
Preferred By Pets 3903 Voltaire St	223-9023
Professional Pet Grooming 1843 Garnet Ave	483-4680
Richlin Farms Pets N' Fish 3840 Valley Center Dr # 601	259-1717
San Diego Pet Club 1210 W Morena Blvd	275-6444
San Diego Pet Supply 4580 Federal Blvd	263-2211
Uptown Pets 1040 University Ave # B101	688-0770

RETAIL - PET SUPPLIES (CONTINUED)
SAN MARCOS

Pet City Inc 1300 E Mission Rd	480-7301
Pet Supply Warehouse 1609 Capalina Rd	752-1300
Ye Olde Poodle Parlour 740 Nordahl Rd	745-9471

SANTEE

Discount Pet Supply 235 Town Center Pky	449-3266
Discount Petmart 9710 Mission Gorge Rd # B	258-1403
Jaws 'N Paws 9844 N Magnolia Ave	449-5301
Safari Pet & Supply 9345 Mission Gorge Rd	449-9494
Teddy's Dog House 8951 Carlton Hills Blvd	448-8633

SOLANA BEACH

Perfect Pet 201 S Highway 101	755-3308

SPRING VALLEY

Casa De Oro Pet Supply & Groom 9905 Campo Rd	462-7300
Grooming By Joyce 577 Sweetwater Rd	464-4373
Plaza Pet 9734 1/2 Campo Rd	466-6320
Rancho San Diego Dog Grooming 10783 Jamacha Blvd	670-4779
Spring Valley Feed & Pet Ctr 435 Sweetwater Rd	479-2420
Sturdy Dog Foods 9124 Olive Dr	463-2573

VISTA

Petsmart 1740 University Dr.	630-3544
Brengle Terrace Animal Hosp 971 Vale Terrace Dr	758-8004
Cal-Vista Animal Hospital 1318 N Santa Fe Ave	726-3222
Country Feed Store 2111 E Vista Way	724-7310
Mac's Pet Supplies 1680 S Melrose Dr	727-2988
Pet Centers 1253 E Vista Way	726-4888
Petco Animal Supplies Inc 244 W Broadway	758-3113
Spicer's Shaggy Dog 1929 W Vista Way	726-7387

TRAINING - BEHAVIORAL
SAN DIEGO

Tree House Animal Foundation (Free)	312-784-5488
Dial-Pet (Free)	312-342-5738
Animal Behavior Helpline (Free)	415-554-3075
American Temperament Test Society	314-225-5346

TRAINING - OBEDIENCE & BEHAVIORAL
ALPINE

Love On A Leash 2241 W Victoria Dr	445-4802

CHULA VISTA

Camp Gober Kennels 33 Palomar St	420-2948

EL CAJON

Academy Of Canine Training Po Box 523	447-1831
Canine Center 535 Floyd Smith Dr	441-9995
Gold Star Kennels 5748 Dehesa Rd	445-2527
Hawaiiana Canine School 13320 Camino Canada # 6	443-7780

ENCINITAS

Animal Keeper 155 Saxony Rd	753-9366

TRAINING - OBEDIENCE & BEHAVIORAL (CONTINUED)

Lu Meyer Obedience Academy 436-3571
464 Cole Ranch Rd

ESCONDIDO
Blazin' Border Collies 739-8673
15671 Old Pasqual Rd

Chosen Dog 749-4235
28683 Mountain Lilac Rd

Personal K-9 Training 743-0318
1733 Tobacco Rd

FALLBROOK
North County Dog Training 728-1003
2272 Glenn Rd

Tiggeroo Kennels
215 W. Fallbrook St. **723-3419**
See our coupon

Welch & Assoc 723-2166
2595 Rainbow Valley Blvd

LA JOLLA
Good Buddies Home Pet Care 453-6857

S D Hunter Retriever Club 459-6614
7514 Girard Ave

OCEANSIDE
Animal Keeper 941-3221
3532 College Blvd

Oceanside Pet Hotel 757-2345
2909 San Luis Rey Rd

POWAY
Animal Keeper 748-9676
12280 Oak Knoll Rd

Good Dog Training School 748-7943
12843 Papago Dr

SAN DIEGO
American Canine Training 274-0268
See our coupon

Anti-Theft K-9 Svc 441-2939
10601 Tierrasanta Blvd # A

Fon-Jon Boarding & Training 273-2266
5050 Santa Fe St

Mc Kee Grooming & Training 560-7636
7729 Othello Ave

SAN MARCOS
A Dog's Life Professional Dog 745-6621
383 Discovery St

San Marcos Training & Boarding 744-5171
130 S Twin Oaks Valley Rd

SOLANA BEACH
Academy Animal Hospital 755-1511
741 Academy Dr

SPRING VALLEY
Jay Bee's Kennels 463-0207
9124 Olive Dr

VISTA
Country Feed Store 724-7310
2111 E Vista Way

NOTES

Every Pet Should Have a Copy!

PetPages *makes a Great Gift For Your Friends and Their Four-legged Friends!*

PetPages is a wonderful gift for any occasion. Additional copies can be ordered directly from the publisher by filling out the order form below and mailing it with check or money order to:

RJLA, Inc.
9921 Carmel Mountain Rd. #303
San Diego, CA. 92129

1-3 copies: $19.95   4-10 copies: $17.95
11+ copies: Call for quantity discounts (619) 484-7930

Name_____
Address_____
City_____ State_____ Zip_____

Please send me _____ copies of PetPages at $_____ each.
Total amount of order $_____.
Check or money order only.
Send to: RJLA, Inc.   9921 Carmel Mountain Rd. #303
San Diego, CA. 92129

Order your new copy each year to receive the most up-to-date pet events, directory, and money saving coupons!

NOTES

Pet Sitters Association of San Diego County

Call 1-800-4-Pet-Sit for the professional sitter nearest you!

Pet Sitters Association of San Diego County

Serving all of San Diego!

Receive $5 OFF Your First Sit.
Not valid with any other offer.

PetPages

EXPIRES DEC. 31, 1997

$5 Savings

"For Pet's Sake"
A quality, affordable, worry-free, in-home pet sitting service.
Reliable & Experienced
Servicing these areas:
Hillcrest, Mission Hills, UTC and Clairemont
Licensed - Bonded - References

Please Call
284-5656
Susan K. Smith
Caregiver

Member of the San Diego Pet Sitters Association

"For Pet's Sake"
A quality, affordable, worry-free, in-home pet sitting service.

You are cordially invited to enjoy $5 OFF an in-home pet sitting.

Member of the San Diego Pet Sitters Association.
Minimum 7 day service

PetPages

EXPIRES DEC. 31, 1997

$5 Savings

Fuerte Animal Hospital

FOR ALL YOUR PET NEEDS!

4620 Avacado Blvd.
La Mesa
440-1432

Fuerte Animal Hospital
La Mesa

You are cordially invited to enjoy these Discounted Vaccines:

DOGS		CATS	
DHLP - Parvo	$12.00	FVRCP	$ 6.00
Corona	$ 6.00	Felix	$12.00
Bordetella	$ 9.50	FIP	$12.00
Lyme	$15.00	Rabies	$ 4.00
Rabies	$ 4.00		

PetPages

EXPIRES DEC. 31, 1997

20% Savings

Pet Sitters Association of San Diego County

Serving all of San Diego County
All our members are *Licensed* and *Bonded*.

**Call
1-800-4-Pet-Sit**
For The Professional Sitter Nearest You!

Use PetPages™ *throughout the year to plan your pet activities and receive great savings!*

"For Pet's Sake"

A quality, affordable, worry-free, in-home pet sitting service.
Reliable & Experienced
Servicing these areas:
Hillcrest, Mission Hills, UTC and Clairemont
Licensed - Bonded
References

Please Call
284-5656
Susan K. Smith
Caregiver
Member of the San Diego Pet Sitters Assoc.

Use PetPages™ *throughout the year to plan your pet activities and receive great savings!*

Fuerte Animal Hospital

For All Your Pet Needs!

4620 Avacado Blvd.
La Mesa
(Avacado Blvd & Fuerte)
440-1432

Call for Appointment
M-F 7:30 am. - 6 pm.
Sat. 7:30 am. - 2 pm

Use PetPages™ *throughout the year to plan your pet activities and receive great savings!*

VAGABOND INNS

Four San Diego Locations!

Mission Valley
297-1691
By the Bay
232-6391
Point Loma
224-3371
Chula Vista
422-8305

VAGABOND INNS — Four San Diego Locations
Mission Valley, By the Bay, Point Loma, Chula Vista

We're Pet Friendly

Call (800) 522-1555 - Mention "PetPages" for discount

PetPages™ EXPIRES DEC. 31, 1997 **10% Savings**

PEE DEE'S PAW PROTECTORS™

Your Dog's Best Friend

Protect your dog's paws from rough, abrasive surfaces, as well as extreme hot and cold conditions. Sizes from x-small to giant.

7416 Altiva Place
Carlsbad, CA. 92009
438-8226

PEE DEE'S PAW PROTECTORS™

Your Dog's Best Friend

Protect your dog's paws from rough, abrasive surfaces, as well as extreme hot and cold conditions. Sizes from x-small to giant.

Receive 20% Off the price of up to three sets of boots.

Not valid with any other offer.

PetPages™ EXPIRES DEC. 31, 1997 **20% Savings**

Parisi's Italian Restaurant

323 Broadway
Chula Vista

420-4490

Parisi's Italian Restaurant

Receive 10% off your meal.

Not valid with any other offers.
Good for Food Only - Not Drinks

PetPages™ EXPIRES DEC. 31, 1997 **10% Savings**

Complimentary continental breakfast, HBO, parking, local calls, swimming pools, weekday newspaper. Children under 18 free with parents. Kitchenettes in some locations. SeaWorld and San Diego Zoo packages available.

Mission Valley, located in Hotel Circle	297-1691
By the Bay, one block from San Diego Harbor	232-6391
Point Loma, located entrance to Shelter Island	224-3371
Chula Vista, San Diego South Bay area	422-8305

Subject to availability. Not available to groups or in conjunction with any other offer or promotion. Must present coupon upon check-in.

Use PetPages™ throughout the year to plan your pet activities and receive great savings!

Your Dog's Best Friend

For more information about
PEE DEE'S PAW PROTECTORS™ or to get sizing information please call or write us at:

PEE DEE'S PAW PROTECTORS™
7416 Altiva Place
Carlsbad, CA. 92009
(619) 438-8226

Use PetPages™ throughout the year to plan your pet activities and receive great savings!

Parisi's Italian Restaurant

Dine in, Take out or Delivery

323 Broadway
Chula Vista
420-4490

Use PetPages™ throughout the year to plan your pet activities and receive great savings!

IMPERIAL BEACH PET HOSPITAL

"We Care"
424-3961
538 12th Street
Imperial Beach
Payment Plans Available
Mastercard/Visa
M-F 7am - 7pm
Sat. 8-6 / Sun. 10-1

IMPERIAL BEACH PET HOSPITAL

We use the "We Care Approach" with all our clients!

FREE PET EXAM FOR NEW CLIENTS WITH THIS COUPON

Not valid with any other offers.
New clients only.

PetPages
EXPIRES DEC. 31, 1997

$20 Savings

Flea-X
The natural way to treat for fleas!

1-800-773-5329
619-233-5329
Guaranteed for one full year
Inside and Outside Treatments.
Don't you deserve a flea-free home?

No More Fleas - Guaranteed
SPECIAL OFFER

ONLY $129.95

Rid your entire home of fleas!
1100 to 1500 sq. ft. home (smaller or larger homes - call for quote)

Save up to $50 while ridding your home of Fleas the Natural Way... With Flea-X

Not valid with other offers.

PetPages
EXPIRES DEC. 31, 1997

Up to $50 Savings

ALWAYS NATURAL
Pet Food & Supplies

FREE HOME DELIVERY

(619) 530-0532

Food, Toys, Grooming Supplies, Treats, Litters, Bedding, Accessories, Small Animal Feeds, Bird Seed & Toys.

ALWAYS NATURAL Pet Food & Supplies

$2.50 off
40 lb. bag premium dog food or
20 lb. bag premium cat food

FREE HOME DELIVERY

- -

$1.00 off
8 lb. or 20 lb. bag premium dog food or
8 lb. bag premium cat food

Not valid with any other offer.

PetPages
EXPIRES DEC. 31, 1997

$3.50 Savings

IMPERIAL BEACH PET HOSPITAL

We use the "We Care Approach" with all our clients!

Payment plans available.
We accept Mastercard & Visa
Mon.-Fri. 7am - 7pm **Sat.** 8am - 6pm **Sun.** 10am - 1pm

538 12th Street, Imperial Beach
424-3961

Use **PetPages**™ *throughout the year to plan your pet activities and receive great savings!*

You Deserve A Pest Free Home!
One application *Guarantees* you a flea-free home for one full year!

Rid your home of harmful fleas the natural way... with **Flea-X**.

- Environmentally Sensible
- No odors - No dust
- No wet carpet
- No need to vacate home during application
- Recommended by veterinarians and groomers
- Full service pest elimination

1-800-773-5329 / 619-233-5329
Lic #BRA398
Visa / MC / Discovery / Amex accepted

Non-Chemical Outside flea treatments available. Call for quote!

Use **PetPages**™ *throughout the year to plan your pet activities and receive great savings!*

WE CARRY: Natural Life, Nature's Recipe, Old Mother Hubbard, Triumph, Nutro, Natural Balance, Wysong, Neura and Iams.

ALSO AVAILABLE:
- Toys
- Treats
- Grooming Supplies
- Litters
- Bedding & Accessories
- Small Animal Feeds
- Bird Seed & Toys

FREE HOME DELIVERY!
Give your back a break!
We'll do the lifting

ALWAYS NATURAL Pet Food & Supplies
(619) 530-0532

Use **PetPages**™ *throughout the year to plan your pet activities and receive great savings!*

A1 Carpet Cleaning

Inland
746-6469
Coastal
967-6860
Bonded & Insured
CA Contractor
Lic. # 720062

A1 VALLEY CENTER

Specializing in
Pet Deodorization
And Disinfectant
Free Estimates
Full Service
Carpet Cleaning

New Carpet and Vinyl Sales

Receive $10 OFF Any Service

Not valid with any other offer.

PetPages™

EXPIRES DEC. 31, 1997

$10 Savings

Pet Express

758-8777

Serving
San Diego
Los Angeles
Orange County
Riverside
San Bernardino

Pet Express

Specializing in Fine Pet Foods

$3 OFF Any 40 lb. Bag of Dog Food

Not valid with any other offer.

PetPages™

EXPIRES DEC. 31, 1997

$3 Savings

San Simeon
Mexican Food

All Natural

Come join us on the coast
944-0565
2035 San Elijo
Cardiff by the Sea

San Simeon
Mexican Food

All Natural

You're invited to receive 10% off your next visit.

Not valid with any other coupon or specials.

PetPages™

EXPIRES DEC. 31, 1997

10% Savings

A1 Factory Direct
Carpet - Vinyl - Tile

Visit our Showroom at
1924-A Commercial
Escondido, CA. 92029

Call for Appointment
Mon-Fri. 8am - 5pm
746-6469 Inland
967-6860 Coastal

Use **PetPages**™ *throughout the year to plan your pet activities and receive great savings!*

Pet Express

1-800-735-PETS

Free Delivery of Any Top of the Line Products:
Anmar • Eqyss • Innova • Sold Gold • Easle
Quest • Matrix • California Natural

Use **PetPages**™ *throughout the year to plan your pet activities and receive great savings!*

San Simeon
Mexican Food
All Natural

- No Lard Used
- Vegetarian Beans Only
- All Fresh Meats & Produce
- All Fresh Cooked
- Chicken is White Meat Only
- Beef is Shredded Steak Only

944-0565
2035 San Elijo, Cardiff by the Sea, CA. 92007

Use **PetPages**™ *throughout the year to plan your pet activities and receive great savings!*

WAG-N-WHEELS
MOBILE PET GROOMING

496-3362

Quality since 1989
Serving
North Coastal, La Jolla &
Rancho Santa Fe
Communities

WAG-N-WHEELS
MOBILE PET GROOMING
Convenient At-your-Home Grooming.
Professional Care & Service
Less Stressful for Your Pet
Less Time Consuming

$3.00 OFF Your First Grooming

PetPages

EXPIRES DEC. 31, 1997

$3 Savings

Valhalla Veterinary Clinic

FOR ALL YOUR PET NEEDS!

1498 Jamacha Rd. # 104
El Cajon

440-1432

Valhalla Veterinary Clinic
El Cajon

You are cordially invited to enjoy these Discounted Vaccines:

DOGS		CATS	
DHLP - Parvo	$12.00	FVRCP	$ 6.00
Corona	$ 6.00	Felix	$12.00
Bordetella	$ 9.50	FIP	$12.00
Lyme	$15.00	Rabies	$ 4.00
Rabies	$ 4.00		

PetPages

EXPIRES DEC. 31, 1997

20% Savings

DEMPSEY'S
Restaurant

5119 1/2 Saratoga Ave
Ocean Beach
222-7740

DEMPSEY'S
Restaurant

Receive $1.00 off your next visit

Not valid with any other offer

PetPages

EXPIRES DEC. 31, 1997

$1 Savings

WAG-N-WHEELS
MOBILE PET GROOMING
496-3362

Quality Since 1989

Serving North County Coastal, La Jolla & Rancho Santa Fe Communities

Use PetPages™ *throughout the year to plan your pet activities and receive great savings!*

Valhalla Veterinary Clinic
FOR ALL YOUR PET NEEDS!

1498 Jamacha Rd. # 104
El Cajon
(Jamacha & Chase)

440-1432

Call for Appointment
M-F 7:30 am. - 6 pm.
Sat. 7:30 am. - 2 pm.

Use PetPages™ *throughout the year to plan your pet activities and receive great savings!*

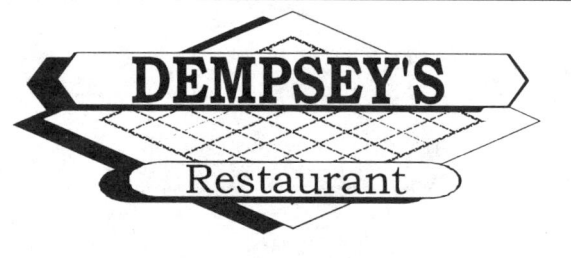

DEMPSEY'S
Restaurant

5119 1/2 Saratoga Ave
Ocean Beach
222-7740

Use PetPages™ *throughout the year to plan your pet activities and receive great savings!*

Day Care For Dogs

- Dogs play freely on a fenced and supervised ranch.
- Pick-up and Delivery
- Overnight Boarding

619-436-1233
Seabreeze Farms
5730 Carmel Valley Rd.

Day Care For Dogs

We spoil your dog on a 74 acre ranch that offers everything dog dreams are made of!

Two Days for the Price of One!

Not valid with any other offer.

PetPages.

EXPIRES DEC. 31, 1997

$25 Savings

GALLEY AT THE MARINA

Find us at the Chula Vista Marina

550 Marina Parkway
Chula Vista, CA. 91910
619-422-5714
fax 619-422-7708

GALLEY AT THE MARINA

MEAL DEAL FOR TWO $5.98

BREAKFAST	LUNCH
• 2 Eggs	• 1/2 Deli Sandwich
• 2 Bacon	• Chips
• Jumbo Pancake	• Homemade Cup of Soup
• Hash Browns and Toast	*Per Person*
Per Person	

Dine in only. Not valid with any other offer

PetPages.

EXPIRES DEC. 31, 1997

$2 Savings

The Animal Keeper

Boarding, Grooming & Training

3 Locations to Serve You

Oceanside
3532 College Blvd. (619) 941-3221
Encinitas
155 Saxony Road (619) 753-9366
Poway
12280 Oak Knoll Rd. (619) 748-9676

Marty Labdon - Director

The Animal Keeper

**$5 Off a Bath & Dip or
A 1 Day Free Board with a 3 night or longer stay.**

Not valid with any other offer.

PetPages.

EXPIRES DEC. 31, 1997

20% Savings

Day Care For Dogs

Dogs play freely on a fenced and supervised ranch.
Pick-up and Delivery • Overnight Boarding
Beach trips & hikes • Trees to nap under • Pools
Cool ocean breezes • Safe agility ramps • Toys • Snacks
Fully Supervised, Licensed and Bonded

619-436-1233

Seabreeze Farms
5730 Carmel Valley Road (3 miles east of Del Mar)

Use **PetPages** *throughout the year to plan your pet activities and receive great savings!*

GALLEY AT THE MARINA

Dinner Specials

Tues: All You Can Eat — **$5.95**
Spaghetti & Meatballs *Includes bread and salad.*

Thurs: Fish & Chips — **$5.95**

550 Marina Parkway (North of Jakes)
Chula Vista Marina   619-422-5714

Use **PetPages** *throughout the year to plan your pet activities and receive great savings!*

The Animal Keeper

Boarding, Grooming & Training

3 Locations to Serve You

Oceanside
3532 College Blvd. (619) 941-3221

Encinitas
155 Saxony Road (619) 753-9366

Poway
12280 Oak Knoll Rd. (619) 748-9676

Use **PetPages** *throughout the year to plan your pet activities and receive great savings!*

HAMILTON CARPET & UPHOLSTERY CLEANING

24 Hour
Flood Service
Guaranteed
Pet Odor Removal

Phone
738-9461
Pager
739-7156

HAMILTON CARPET & UPHOLSTERY CLEANING

| 3 Rooms and a Hallway $49.95 | 5 Rooms and a Hallway $79.95 |

Service Includes: Prescrub, Deodorizing, Basic Spot Removal

Not valid with any other offers.

$15 Savings

PetPages.

EXPIRES DEC. 31, 1997

PENASQUITOS PET CLINIC
Sharon Sprouse, DVM

For the caring service your pet deserves!
484-1260
9728 Carmel Mtn. Rd.
Mon: 7:30 - 7:00
T, TH, Fri: 7:30 - 6:00
Wed: 7:30 - 1:00
Sat: 8:00 - Noon

PENASQUITO PET CLINIC
Sharon Sprouse, DVM

For the caring service your pet deserves!

Pay only $10 for your pet's initial exam

New Clients Only.
Not valid with any other offer.

$12 Savings

PetPages.

EXPIRES DEC. 31, 1997

PENASQUITOS PET CLINIC
Sharon Sprouse, DVM

For the caring service your pet deserves!
484-1260
9728 Carmel Mtn. Rd.
Mon: 7:30 - 7:00
T, TH, Fri: 7:30 - 6:00
Wed: 7:30 - 1:00
Sat: 8:00 - Noon

PENASQUITO PET CLINIC
Sharon Sprouse, DVM

| **$15 OFF Dental** Mon. - Tues., Thurs. - Fri. (Reg. Price - Dog $95, Cat $85) Includes: Free exam, anesthesia, dental cleaning, ultra sonic scaling & polishing. | **$10 OFF Spay** **$5 OFF Neuter** *Dog or Cat* |

Not valid with any other offer.
One coupon per visit.

Up to $35 Savings

PetPages.

EXPIRES DEC. 31, 1997

HAMILTON CARPET & UPHOLSTERY CLEANING

Additional Services:
- ♦ Guaranteed Pet Odor Removal
- ♦ Speed Drying
- ♦ Teflon Protection
- ♦ Flood Service
- ♦ Truck Mounted Unit

Phone
738-9461

Pager
739-7156

Use **PetPages**™ *throughout the year to plan your pet activities and receive great savings!*

PENASQUITO PET CLINIC
Sharon Sprouse, DVM

We Now Do Boarding - Call For Rates
See Our New Expanded Facilities

484-1260
9728 Carmel Mountain Rd.
Mon: 7:30 a.m. - 7 p.m.
Tues, Thurs, Fri: 7:30 a.m. - 6 p.m.
Wed: 7:30 a.m. - 1 p.m.
Sat: 8 a.m. - Noon

Use **PetPages**™ *throughout the year to plan your pet activities and receive great savings!*

PENASQUITO PET CLINIC
Sharon Sprouse, DVM

We Now Do Boarding - Call For Rates
See Our New Expanded Facilities

484-1260
9728 Carmel Mountain Rd.
Mon: 7:30 a.m. - 7 p.m.
Tues, Thurs, Fri: 7:30 a.m. - 6 p.m.
Wed: 7:30 a.m. - 1 p.m.
Sat: 8 a.m. - Noon

Use **PetPages**™ *throughout the year to plan your pet activities and receive great savings!*

EAGLE NEST BED & BREAKFAST

Pets are always welcome!

Victorian Style Home
Full Breakfast
Full Service
1/2 Acre Fenced Yard
Pool & Jacuzzi

**619-765-1252 or
1-888-EGLNEST**(toll free)
2609 D St.

EAGLE NEST BED & BREAKFAST

We Love Pets!
Don't Kennel Your Friend,
Bring Him With You.

Receive 50% Off Your Second Night.

Not valid with any other offer

PetPages.

EXPIRES DEC. 31, 1997

50% Savings

U.S. GRANT
Four Star & Four Diamond Pampering!

326 Broadway
San Diego, CA. 92101

619-232-3121
800-237-5029

Experience the
U.S. Grant's Pampered Pet

Receive 10% off Regular Rates

Not valid for groups, citywide conventions, special events or with any other offer.

PetPages.

EXPIRES DEC. 31, 1997

10% Savings

Metaphor Cafe & Bistro

Outside & Inside Dining

258 E. 2nd Ave
Escondido
489-8890

Metaphor Cafe & Bistro

Buy one drink for regular price get a second for 50% off.

Not valid with any other offer.

PetPages.

EXPIRES DEC. 31, 1997

Up to **$2** Savings

VICTORIAN STYLE HOME WITHIN WALKING DISTANCE TO ALL DOWNTOWN JULIAN!

Full Service • Full Breakfast • Pool & Jacuzzi
1/2 Acre Fenced Yard • Beautiful Views

Treat yourself to a *Special Time* in a Special Place.

EAGLE NEST BED & BREAKFAST
2609 D St. Julian, CA
1-888-EGLNEST or 619-765-1252

Use **PetPages** *throughout the year to plan your pet activities and receive great savings!*

PAMPERED PET PROGRAM

Now your beloved pet can receive celebrated Four Star and Four Diamond pampering just like you.
We provide pet walking services and arrange grooming appointments as well as the following:

For "Man's Best Friend"
Soft sleeping pillow • Chef prepared gourmet dinners
Rawhide "chewy" bones • Turn down biscuit

For "The Favorite Feline"
Welcome warm bowl of milk • Squeaky catnip toys
Scratching post • Fresh box of liter

This service is free of charge and based on space availability.

A Historical Hotel with 280 Guest Rooms
326 Broadway, San Diego, CA. 92101 (Downtown)
619-232-3121   800-237-5029

Use **PetPages** *throughout the year to plan your pet activities and receive great savings!*

Metaphor Cafe & Bistro

Serving your favorite coffee drinks along with beer and wine.
Breakfast, Lunch and Dinner
Live Music Most Nights
258 E. 2nd Ave
(Located in Downtown Escondido)
489-8890

Use **PetPages** *throughout the year to plan your pet activities and receive great savings!*

DEXTER'S DELI
NATURAL GOURMET DOG TREATS & ACCESSORIES

792-3707

Located in the heart of Del Mar
1229 Camino Del Mar
(between 12th & 13th)

Where Humans Are Always Welcome!

DEXTER'S DELI
NATURAL GOURMET DOG TREATS & ACCESSORIES

792-3707

- Fresh Baked Natural Dog Treats
- Dog & Cat Foods
- Self-Service Pet Wash
- Supplies & Whimsical Gifts

Receive $2.00 off with purchase of $15.00 or more.

Not valid with any other offer.

PetPages

EXPIRES DEC. 31, 1997

$2 Savings

CARDIFF ANIMAL HOSPITAL

Dogs, Cats, Birds, Exotic & Reptile

Please Call For An Appointment
436-3215
2159 San Elijo Ave
Cardiff by the Sea

CARDIFF ANIMAL HOSPITAL

$3.00 Off
EACH VACCINE
(Exam must be current)
Present coupon when checking in pet.

Not valid with any other offer.

PetPages

EXPIRES DEC. 31, 1997

Up to $3 Savings

CARDIFF ANIMAL HOSPITAL

Dogs, Cats, Birds, Exotic & Reptile

Please Call For An Appointment
436-3215
2159 San Elijo Ave
Cardiff by the Sea

CARDIFF ANIMAL HOSPITAL

$5.00 Off
PHYSICAL EXAM OR GROOMING
Dogs, Cats, Birds, Reptiles
Present coupon when checking in pet.

Not valid with any other offer.

PetPages

EXPIRES DEC. 31, 1997

Up to $5 Savings

"THE STORE WHERE HUMANS ARE ALWAYS WELCOME."

Freshly Baked Natural Dog Treats
Highest Quality Dog & Cat Foods • Whimsical Gifts
Handmade Dog Bowls • Dog Toys • Cool Collars
Iams • Nutro Max • Hund-N-Flocken • Eukanuba
Nature's Recipe • Science Diet • Wysong

Located in the heart of Del Mar
1229 Camino Del Mar
(2 blks south of the Plaza between 12th & 13th)

ALL NATURAL
ALL THE TIME

Use **PetPages™** *throughout the year to plan your pet activities and receive great savings!*

CARDIFF
ANIMAL HOSPITAL

Dr. Monica Laflin
Dr. Sue Redpath
Dr. Katherine Allen

DOGS, CATS, BIRDS, EXOTIC & REPTILE
• Flea Control • Accupuncture Treatment
• PennHip X-rays • Spay & Neutering
• Grooming • Full Medical/Surgical Care
Please Call For Appointment
436-3215
2159 San Elijo Ave. Cardiff by the Sea

Use **PetPages™** *throughout the year to plan your pet activities and receive great savings!*

CARDIFF
ANIMAL HOSPITAL

Dr. Monica Laflin
Dr. Sue Redpath
Dr. Katherine Allen

DOGS, CATS, BIRDS, EXOTIC & REPTILE
• Flea Control • Accupuncture Treatment
• PennHip X-rays • Spay & Neutering
• Grooming • Full Medical/Surgical Care
Please Call For Appointment
436-3215
2159 San Elijo Ave. Cardiff by the Sea

Use **PetPages™** *throughout the year to plan your pet activities and receive great savings!*

Blossom Valley Groom and Board

A Clean, Fresh Environment for the Pet You Love!

(619) 443-4271
9400 Blossom Valley Rd.,
El Cajon, CA. 92921

Blossom Valley Groom and Board

Receive $5.00 off any boarding, bathing or grooming service.

Not valid with any other offers.

PetPages

EXPIRES DEC. 31, 1997

$5 Savings

SPRING CREEK KENNEL & CATTERY

Providing loving attention and care for your pet!

(619) 463-1722

9279 Campo Rd.

SPRING CREEK KENNEL & CATTERY

Your pet deserves a treat - a bone, a bath, a weekend retreat!

Receive $5.00 off any boarding, bathing or grooming service.

Not valid with any other offer.

PetPages

EXPIRES DEC. 31, 1997

$5 Savings

AMERICAN CANINE TRAINING

Training Done With Care and Affection

Obedience Training
Protection Training
Behavior Modification
Customized Problem Solving

619-274-0268

AMERICAN CANINE TRAINING

The Best Present You Can Give Your Dog Is An Education

RECEIVE A COMPLEMENTARY CONSULTATION

Not valid with any other offer.

PetPages

EXPIRES DEC. 31, 1997

$50 Savings

Blossom Valley Groom and Board

- All tours, grooming and boarding done by appointment only.
- Outside exercise area for "playtimes".
- Large dog enclosures for Fido.
- Separate "house cattery" for Kitty.
- **A Clean, Fresh Environment for the Pet You Love!**

9400 Blossom Valley Rd, El Cajon.
From Hwy. 8 exit on Lake Jennings Park Rd. Go north and turn right at light.
619-443-4271

Use
PetPages™
throughout the year to plan your pet activities and receive great savings!

SPRING CREEK KENNEL & CATTERY

Providing loving attention and care for your pet in your absence.
Boarding, bathing, grooming, training, pick up and delivery service.
A clean, fresh environment for the pet you love. Tours Welcome!

Open 9-6 Mon.-Sat.
Closed Major Holidays and Sundays.
Please call for directions.
(619) 463-1722

Use
PetPages™
throughout the year to plan your pet activities and receive great savings!

AMERICAN CANINE TRAINING

The Best Present You Can Give Your Dog Is An Education
We've trained over 1000 Dogs. Done with care and affection.
Positive Motivation Techniques Always Used
Obedience Training Protection Training Behavior Modification
Customized Problem Solving

619-274-0268

Use
PetPages™
throughout the year to plan your pet activities and receive great savings!

MISSION
Carpet and
Upholstery Cleaning

*Pet odor control
Carpet deodorizing
Carpet repairs
Red stains removed
Water damage repair
Window cleaning*

Coastal
259-0557

Inland
480-0905

MISSION
Carpet and Upholstery Cleaning
*Pet odor control   Carpet deodorizing
Carpet repairs   Red stains removed
Water damage repair   Window cleaning*

Receive 20% OFF Your Carpet Cleaning

Not valid with any other offer.

PetPages.

EXPIRES DEC. 31, 1997

Up to **$20** Savings

MISSION
Carpet and
Upholstery Cleaning

*Pet odor control
Carpet deodorizing
Carpet repairs
Red stains removed
Water damage repair
Window cleaning*

Coastal
259-0557

Inland
480-0905

MISSION
Carpet and Upholstery Cleaning
*Pet odor control   Carpet deodorizing
Carpet repairs   Red stains removed
Water damage repair   Window cleaning*

Receive 20% OFF Your Carpet Cleaning

Not valid with any other offer.

PetPages.

EXPIRES DEC. 31, 1997

Up to **$20** Savings

DEXTER'S DELI
NATURAL GOURMET DOG
TREATS & ACCESSORIES

792-3707

Located in the heart of Del Mar
1229 Camino Del Mar
(between 12th & 13th)

Where Humans Are Always Welcome!

DEXTER'S DELI
NATURAL GOURMET DOG
TREATS & ACCESSORIES

792-3707

FRESH BAKED NATURAL DOG TREATS

DOG & CAT FOODS

SELF-SERVICE PET WASH

SUPPLIES & WHIMSICAL GIFTS

Receive $2.00 off with purchase of $15.00 or more.

Not valid with any other offer.

PetPages.

EXPIRES DEC. 31, 1997

$2 Savings

MISSION
Carpet and Upholstery Cleaning
Pet odor control   Carpet deodorizing
Carpet repairs   Red stains removed
Water damage repair   Window cleaning

Coastal   **Inland**
259-0557   480-0905

Use **PetPages** *throughout the year to plan your pet activities and receive great savings!*

MISSION
Carpet and Upholstery Cleaning
Pet odor control   Carpet deodorizing
Carpet repairs   Red stains removed
Water damage repair   Window cleaning

Coastal   **Inland**
259-0557   480-0905

Use **PetPages** *throughout the year to plan your pet activities and receive great savings!*

"THE STORE WHERE HUMANS ARE ALWAYS WELCOME."

Freshly Baked Natural Dog Treats
Highest Quality Dog & Cat Foods • Whimsical Gifts
Handmade Dog Bowls • Dog Toys • Cool Collars
Iams • Nutro Max • Hund-N-Flocken • Eukanuba
Nature's Recipe • Science Diet • Wysong

Located in the heart of Del Mar
1229 Camino Del Mar
(2 blks south of the Plaza between 12th & 13th)
792-3707

ALL NATURAL
ALL THE TIME

Use **PetPages** *throughout the year to plan your pet activities and receive great savings!*

TIGGEROO KENNELS

Private-in-home Training
Group Classes
Puppy Classes
Private Obedience Classes
Junior Obedience

Bob Baker
Leslie C. Baker
Dog Trainers
Public Obedience
Family Protection
723-3419
215 W. Fallbrook St., Fallbrook

TIGGEROO KENNELS

First lesson Complimentary, Plus receive 15% off either private training or group classes.

Not valid with any other offers.

PetPages™   EXPIRES DEC. 31, 1997   **15% Savings**

Potato Shack

Dogs -
Bring your Masters!
All the water you can drink.
Outside Dining Only

Encinitas Location Only

120 W. I St.
Encinitas

Potato Shack

Receive 10% off your meal Plus *All You Can Eat American Fries!* Encinitas Location Only

Not Valid with any other offers.
Expires Dec 31, 1996

PetPages™   EXPIRES DEC. 31, 1997   **10% Savings**

THE DUCHESS COFFEE HOUSE, DELI & CAFE

Furry Friends Welcome

Bands/Music on Fri. & Sat. Nights

247 3rd. Ave
Chula Vista
498-1847

THE DUCHESS COFFEE HOUSE, DELI & CAFE

Hip-Hip Hooray!   **Receive 10% off your next order.**

Not valid with any other offers.

PetPages™   EXPIRES DEC. 31, 1997   **10% Savings**

TIGGEROO KENNELS

Tired of your dog walking you?
Let us show you a better way to enjoy that Special

We will teach your dog the same program Army & Police shepards go through, (basic obedience). Your dog will learn every command (verbal & hand signals). *No more jumpy, disobedient dog.*
Private-in-home training, group classes, puppy classes.

Come visit or call us at:
215 W. Fallbrook St. - Fallbrook
723-3419 ask for Bob or Leslie

Use PetPages™ throughout the year to plan your pet activities and receive great savings!

Potato Shack

Dogs - Bring your masters to breakfast or lunch!

Enjoy Outside Dining (Dogs)
All The Water You Can Drink!

Open 7 am to 2 pm Daily

120 W. I St. Encinitas (by the LumberYard)   436-1282
Coupon Valid Mon.-Fri. Only.

Use PetPages™ throughout the year to plan your pet activities and receive great savings!

THE DUCHESS COFFEE HOUSE, DELI & CAFE

Hip-Hip HOORAY!

Bands/Music on Fri. & Sat. Nights!
Bring your furry friends.

247 3rd Ave. Chula Vista
498-1847

Use PetPages™ throughout the year to plan your pet activities and receive great savings!

Grooming by Beth

- Professional All-Breed Grooming
- Organic Shampoos and Flea Control

432-0877
at Hwy 78 & Nordahl
in San Marcos

Grooming by Beth

| **$5 OFF** First Grooming | **$5 OFF** Second Grooming |

North County's Only N.C.M.G. thru the Natl. Dog Groomers Assoc.

Not valid with any other offers

PetPages

EXPIRES DEC. 31, 1997

Up to **$10** Savings

DORINDA'S PRETTY PUP GROOMING

447-7366

We Specialize in Pampering Your Pet!

1325 East Main
El Cajon, CA. 92921

DORINDA'S PRETTY PUP GROOMING

Dorinda invites your pet to experience a Full Grooming for 10% off.

Valid for First Time Pet Visits Only.
Located in El Cajon

PetPages

EXPIRES DEC. 31, 1997

$5 Savings

San Simeon
Mexican Food

All Natural

Come join us on the coast

944-0565

2035 San Elijo
Cardiff by the Sea

San Simeon
Mexican Food

All Natural

You're invited to receive 10% off your next visit.
Not valid with any other coupon or specials.

PetPages

EXPIRES DEC. 31, 1997

10% Savings

Grooming by Beth

- Professional All-Breed Grooming
- Organic Shampoos and Flea Control
- Sunday Appointments Available
- Ask about our regular client disounts

North County's only N.C.M.G.
thru the National Dog Groomers Association
432-0877
at Hwy 78 & Nordahl in San Marcos

Use **PetPages™** throughout the year to plan your pet activities and receive great savings!

DORINDA'S PRETTY PUP GROOMING

Specializing in Pampering Your Pet!
Hair, Nails, Flea Treatments

Call Us Today to Schedule an Appointment.
447-7366
Located in El Cajon at 1325 East Main

Use **PetPages™** throughout the year to plan your pet activities and receive great savings!

San Simeon Mexican Food
All Natural

- No Lard Used
- Vegetarian Beans Only
- All Fresh Meats & Produce
- All Fresh Cooked
- Chicken is White Meat Only
- Beef is Shredded Steak Only

944-0565
2035 San Elijo, Cardiff by the Sea, CA. 92007

Use **PetPages™** throughout the year to plan your pet activities and receive great savings!

University Animal Clinic

7134 University Ave.
La Mesa 91941

DR. ROBERT E. LARSSON

(619) 463-9861
24 Hour Emergency Help

Hours:
Mon - Fri 7:30 am. - 6:00 pm.
Sat 9:00 am - 12:00 pm.

University Animal Clinic
La Mesa

20% OFF Dental Cleaning

Free *First* Exam
($19.50 Value)

20% Discount for Existing Clients

Must present coupon at time of visit. One coupon per visit.

PetPages™

EXPIRES DEC. 31, 1997

Up to **$19.50** Savings

Del Norte Plaza Veterinary Clinic

Small Animal Medicine & Surgery
Dogs-Cats-Reptiles
Birds-Exotics

Dr. Rick Lindbeck
New Owner
(Open 6 days a week)
Mon - Fri 8:30-6 Sat 9-3
Shot Clinic - Saturdays 12-3
Spay & Nueter Clinic - Tues & Thurs

(619) 741-VETS (8387)

306 -F West El Norte Parkway - Escondido
In the Vons/Savon Shopping Center

Del Norte Plaza Veterinary Clinic

Small Animal Medicine and Surgery
Dogs - Cats - Reptiles - Birds - Exotics
LOCATED IN ESCONDIDO

Enjoy $10 OFF Your Initial Visit.

Valid for first time pet visits only.

PetPages™

EXPIRES DEC. 31, 1997

$10 Savings

VILLAGE SQUARE ANIMAL HOSPITAL
Dr. Nancy Bushnell

1466 Encinitas Blvd.
Encinitas, CA
(Near El Camino Real
next to 7-11)

(619) 942-1220

Quality Conscientious
Care for Your Pet!

VILLAGE SQUARE ANIMAL HOSPITAL

cordially invites your DOG OR CAT to our

WELLNESS PROGRAM

Consisting of all the recommended yearly vaccinations
(See Reverse Side For The Complete List)

Located in Encinitas

PetPages™

EXPIRES DEC. 31, 1997

Up to **$25** Savings

University Animal Clinic
DR. ROBERT E. LARSSON
7134 University Ave. La Mesa 91941
(619) 463-9861
24 Hour Emergency Help

Dogs - Cats - Birds - Small Animals - Reptiles - Exotics
Dentistry, Skin Problems, Medical, Surgery

Hours: Mon - Fri 7:30 am. - 6:00 pm.
Sat 9:00 am - 12:00 pm.
Please call for an appointment
Major credit cards accepted and *Instant Credit Available*
Member A.V.M.A. & C.V.M.A.

Use **PetPages** *throughout the year to plan your pet activities and receive great savings!*

Del Norte Plaza Veterinary Clinic
Small Animal Medicine and Surgery
Dogs - Cats - Reptiles - Birds - Exotics

New Owner - Dr. Rick Lindbeck
(Open 6 days a week)
Mon - Fri 8:30 am to 6:00 pm **Sat** 9:00 am to 3:00 pm

Shot Clinic - Saturdays 12:00 - 3:00
Spay & Neuter Clinic - Tuesdays & Thursdays
(619) 741-VETS (8387)
306 -F West El Norte Parkway - Escondido CA. 92026
In the Vons/Savon Shopping Center - El Norte Pkwy & Center City Pkwy

Use **PetPages** *throughout the year to plan your pet activities and receive great savings!*

WELLNESS PROGRAM

DOGS $81 *($23 savings)*	**CATS** $44 *($10 savings)*
Physical Exam & Consultation	Physical Exam & Consultation
DHL-P	FVR-CP
Parvo	Pneumonitis (Chlamydiosis)
Corona	Fecal exam
Bordetella	*Recommended for Outside Cats:*
Fecal exam	$31 *($10 savings)*
Heartworm test	Feline Leukemia
Rabies *(additional if needed)*	FIP
	Rabies

VILLAGE SQUARE ANIMAL HOSPITAL
Dr. Nancy Bushnell
1466 Encinitas Blvd. Encinitas, CA (near El Camino Real)
(619) 942-1220

Use **PetPages** *throughout the year to plan your pet activities and receive great savings!*

Metaphor Cafe & Bistro

Outside & Inside Dining

258 E. 2nd Ave
Escondido
489-8890

Metaphor Cafe & Bistro

Buy one drink for regular price get a second for 50% off.

Not valid with any other offer.

PetPages.

EXPIRES DEC. 31, 1997

Up to **$2** Savings

Let your pet get the <u>most</u> from their meal!

The Vittles Vault™

Two sizes available
Holds: 10 lbs. 17.99
       25 lbs. 19.99

To Order Please Call:
1-(800) 842-6543
(24 hours a day!)
GAMMA PLASTICS
Credit cards accepted

The Vittles Vault™
The World's Best Pet Food Container!

- Keeps Food Fresh & Healthy
- Pest-proof (insect & rodents)
- Seals-in "Crunch"
- Airtight
- 2 Size
- NEW!

Holds:
10 lbs. $17.99
25 lbs. $19.99
plus shipping

FREE MEASURING CUP & ID LABEL!
(with purchase)

NO MORE STALE FOOD!!

PetPages.

EXPIRES DEC. 31, 1997

$3.50 Savings

Parisi's Italian Restaurant

**323 Broadway
Chula Vista**

420-4490

Parisi's Italian Restaurant

Receive 10% off your meal.

Not valid with any other offers.
Good for Food Only - Not Drinks

PetPages.

EXPIRES DEC. 31, 1997

10% Savings

Metaphor Cafe & Bistro

Serving your favorite coffee drinks along with beer and wine.

Breakfast, Lunch and Dinner
Live Music Most Nights
258 E. 2nd Ave
(Located in Downtown Escondido)
489-8890

Use **PetPages™** *throughout the year to plan your pet activities and receive great savings!*

The Vittles Vault™
The World's Best Pet Food Container!

The first complete storage system for dry pet foods. No more bulky, awkward bags exposing food to air, excessive moisture & pests. With a spin of the unique lid, the Vittles Vault™ locks in freshness and flavor. Great for natural foods that are nutrient rich and preservative free. Made of food grade high-impact plastic. Several sizes are available. Let your pets get the most from their meal!

1-(800) 842-6543

Use **PetPages™** *throughout the year to plan your pet activities and receive great savings!*

Parisi's Italian Restaurant

Dine in, Take out or Delivery

323 Broadway
Chula Vista
420-4490

Use **PetPages™** *throughout the year to plan your pet activities and receive great savings!*

EMERGENCY INFORMATION

Keep an emergency care information card in your wallet and posted in your home.

List on the card the telephone numbers and addresses of people who should be contacted in case something should happen to you or your pet. Provide all relevant information about your pets in case you are unable to care for them after an emergency.

PET EMERGENCY CARE FORM

In case of Emergency Notify:

(Name) _____ (Phone) _____

Pet Name(s) _____

Veterinarian _____ (Phone) _____

Vet. Address _____

Owner's Name _____

Owner's Phone(s) _____

Addl. Contact _____ (Phone) _____

Cut along dotted line then place in your wallet and post in your home.

EMERGENCY INFORMATION

Keep an emergency care information card in your wallet and posted in your home.

List on the card the telephone numbers and addresses of people who should be contacted in case something should happen to you or your pet. Provide all relevant information about your pets in case you are unable to care for them after an emergency.

PET EMERGENCY CARE FORM

In case of Emergency Notify:

(Name) _____ (Phone) _____

Pet Name(s) _____

Veterinarian _____ (Phone) _____

Vet. Address _____

Owner's Name _____

Owner's Phone(s) _____

Addl. Contact _____ (Phone) _____

Cut along dotted line then place in your wallet and post in your home.

EMERGENCY INFORMATION

Keep an emergency care information card in your wallet and posted in your home.

List on the card the telephone numbers and addresses of people who should be contacted in case something should happen to you or your pet. Provide all relevant information about your pets in case you are unable to care for them after an emergency.

PET EMERGENCY CARE FORM

In case of Emergency Notify:

(Name) _____ (Phone) _____

Pet Name(s) _____

Veterinarian _____ (Phone) _____

Vet. Address _____

Owner's Name _____

Owner's Phone(s) _____

Addl. Contact _____ (Phone) _____

Cut along dotted line then place in your wallet and post in your home.

ADDITIONAL INFORMATION

Addtl. Contact _____ (Phone) _____

Special Needs _____

_____

_____

_____

_____

HAVE FUN BUT BE SAFE!

ADDITIONAL INFORMATION

Addtl. Contact _____ (Phone) _____

Special Needs _____

_____

_____

_____

_____

HAVE FUN BUT BE SAFE!

ADDITIONAL INFORMATION

Addtl. Contact _____ (Phone) _____

Special Needs _____

_____

_____

_____

_____

HAVE FUN BUT BE SAFE!

Pet Pages

NOTES

Pet Pages

NOTES